LIE GROUPS: HISTORY, FRONTIERS

AND APPLICATIONS

VOLUME III

SOPHUS LIE'S 1884 DIFFERENTIAL
INVARIANT PAPER

TRANSLATED BY M. ACKERMAN

COMMENTS AND ADDITIONAL MATERIAL
BY ROBERT HERMANN

MATH SCI PRESS

53 JORDAN ROAD
BROOKLINE, MA. 02146 (USA)

(In part a translation of "On Differential Invariants",
by S. Lie, Math. Annallen,
Vol. 24 (1884), 537-578)

ISBN   0-915692-13-9
Library of Congress Catalog Card Number 75-43189

MATH SCI PRESS
53 Jordan Road
Brookline, Massachusetts 02146

Printed in the United States of America

# PREFACE

In this second volume of Translation and Commentary I begin development of that part of Lie's work that has the greatest scientific import--the relation between group theory and differential equations.

To have a perspective on this work, it is useful to think of analogies between the history of analysis and geometry. For analysis, one sees relatively clearly the outline of the historical development. First, Newton and Leibniz, then the completion of their "revolution" in the 18-th century by Euler, Lagrange, etc., then the magnificent progress through the 190th century--Gauss, Abel, Cauchy, Riemann, Weirstrass, Hilbert,... .

For the purpose of my analogy, focus on the difference in analysis between Euler and Weirstrass. Euler created many ideas and concepts, while Weirstrass emphasized precision of the intellectual tools and language, consolidating the brilliant ideas of the 18-th and early 19-th centuries.

Differential geometry has a much less clearly defined historical structure, which I am not at all prepared to present in detail. However, I believe that only in the last thirty years, with the development of differential manifold theory, have we reached the Weirstrassian stage. Lie is clearly our Euler!

In reading Lie's work in preparation for my commentary on these translations, I was overwhelmed by the richness and beauty of the geometric ideas flowing from Lie's work. Only a small part of this has been absorbed into mainstream mathematics. He thought and wrote in grandiose terms, in a style that has now gone out of fashion, and that would be censored by our scientific journals! The papers translated here and in the succeeding volumes of our Translations present Lie in his wildest and greatest form.

As in Volume I, my comments contain certain new or improved material that can serve as a basis for further research. For example, Chapter D contains a general approach to Lie's whole work on differential equations and symmetries. The key idea is that one should study the structure of the orbit space of a symmetry group on the space of solutions. The "differential invariants" play the same role as the "algebraic invariants" play in the study of orbits of Lie groups acting on finite dimensional spaces. Thus, I see Lie's work leading ultimately to profound new ideas concerning groups acting on infinite dimensional spaces. In Chapter E I sketch development of related ideas concerning Galois theory-- as I have already emphasized, Lie thought of himself as the successor to Abel and Galois, doing for differential equations what they had done for algebraic equations. What has survived

iii

into present times (the so-called "Picard-Vessiot theory" as
a part of "differential algebra") is but an infinitesimal
part of what Lie had in mind.  The implications for applications (e.g., elementary particle physics, continuum mechanics,
systems theory,...) in completely working out Lie's (and
Cartan's) ideas might be sensational.

I apologize that I have done such a poor job in referring
to the modern work on Lie's ideas.  In mitigation, all I can
say is that non-trivial labor has been required for me to
reach this minimal level of understanding!  In particular,
there are two magnificent recent treatises that I have not
used at all, but which I recommend to the reader--Spivak's
Great American Differential Geometry Novel [1] and Kumpera's
impressive scholarly treatment [1] of the Lie theory in a
more abstract and contemporary language than I use here.
Overriding all else, there is the work of D.C. Spencer and
his school on the modern ramifications of the work of Lie and
Cartan.  In fact, I am a student of Spencer, and have uncon-
sciously absorbed many of his ideas!  I will take this opportunity to officially thank him.

Again, I thank Dr. Michael Ackerman (for his translations)
and Karin Young (for her typing)!

# TABLE OF CONTENTS

Page

PREFACE                                                          iii

Chapter A:   CONTACT MANIFOLDS AND MAPPING ELEMENT
             SPACES                                                1

    1. Introduction                                                1
    2. Mappings which Agree to the r-th Order                       2
    3. A Multilinear Algebraic Formula for Differen-
       tials of Maps Between Vector Spaces                          6
    4. Mapping Element Spaces                                       9
    5. Differentiable Subsets of Manifolds                         12
    6. Differential Equations and Contact Transforma-
       tions                                                       13
    7. Contact Element Spaces                                      14
    8. The Mapping Element Spaces as Open Subsets of
       the Contact Spaces                                          19
    9. Prolongation of Group and Lie Algebra Actions               25


ON DIFFERENTIAL INVARIANTS   by Sophus Lie                         29

Chapter 1:   INTRODUCTORY REMARKS                                  31

    1.1                                                            31
    1.2  Differential Invariants                                   32


Chapter 2:   FUNCTIONS AND EQUATIONS WHICH ADMIT A
             FINITE CONTINUOUS GROUP                               35

    2.1  Origins of Transformation Group Theory                    35
    2.2  Differential Equations of Invariants                      40
    2.3  Surfaces which Admit Groups                               45
    2.4  Relation to Algebraic Invariant Theory                    48


Chapter 3:   DIFFERENTIAL INVARIANTS OF CONTINUOUS
             FINITE GROUPS                                         51

    3.1  My Work on Differential Invariants                        51
    3.2  Halphen's Work on Differential Invariants                 55
    3.3  The Complete System of Equations for the
         Differential Invariants                                   58
    3.4  Comments on Chapter 3                                     63

Page

Chapter 4:  DIFFERENTIAL INVARIANTS OF INFINITE
            CONTINUOUS GROUPS                              69

    4.1  Infinite Continuous Groups                       69
    4.2  Examples                                         79
    4.3  The Group of Volume-Preserving Transforma-
         tions of the Plane                               90
    4.4  A General Procedure for Proving Existence
         of Differential Invariants                       98
    4.5  Differential Invariants of Secondary,
         Ordinary Differential Equations                 104
    4.6  Differential Invariants of Point Trans-
         formations                                      110
    4.7  Continuation                                    111
    4.8  Higher Order Ordinary Differential
         Equations                                       112
    4.9  Invariants of a Second Order, Non-Linear
         Equation                                        113
    4.10 A Group Acting on a Special Type of Second
         Order, Ordinary Differential Equation           114
    4.11 Differential Invariants of Second Order
         Partial Differential Equations                  116
    4.12 Invariant Theory of Some Special Second
         Order Partial Differential Equations            122
    4.13 Invariant Theory of Linear Ordinary Differ-
         ential Equations                                124
    4.14 Linear Second Order Partial Differential
         Equations                                       125
    4.15 Curvature as a Differential Invariant           126
    4.16 Invariant Theory of First Order Partial
         Differential Equations                          137
    4.17 Continuation                                    138

Chapter 5:  CONCLUDING REMARKS                           141

    5.1  The Equivalence Problem                         141

Chapter B:  FURTHER WORK IN THE THEORY OF DIFFEREN-
            TIAL INVARIANTS                               149

    1. Differential Invariants and Differential
       Operators                                         149
    2. Algebraic and Differential Invariants of
       the One-Variable Projective Group                 153

Page

3. The Infinite Lie Group Which Preserves the
   Class of Linear Differential Operators              169
4. The Schwartzian Derivative as Differential
   Invariants of the Wilczynski group                 176
5. The Method of Semi-Invariants in Invariant
   Theory                                             184

Chapter C:  INTEGRAL INVARIANTS                        187

1. Introduction                                        187
2. Lagrangians for Fiber Spaces                        189
3. Lagrangians and Variational Problems for
   Mapping Element Spaces                              190
4. Symmetries (In the Sense of Lie) of Variational Problems                                     193
5. Symmetries of Lagrangians of the Form
   $\int L(x,y,y')\,dx$                                195
6. The Cartan Form and the Condition for Lie
   Symmetry of a Variational Problem                   204

Chapter D:  DIFFERENTIAL INVARIANTS AND GROUPS OF
            SYMMETRIES OF DIFFERENTIAL EQUATIONS       211

1. Introduction                                        211
2. Affine Symmetries of Linear, Inhomogeneous
   Second Order Differential Equations                 212
3. The General Lie Theory for Groups of
   Symmetries of Ordinary Differential Equations       219
4. Integrating Factors for First Order, Ordinary
   Differential Equations                              223
5. A Pfaffian System Framework in Which to Study
   First Order Differential Equations                  227
6. Second Order Ordinary Differential Equations
   which Admit One-Parameter Groups of Symmetries      232
7. Second Order Ordinary Differential Equations
   which Admit Two-Dimensional Lie Algebras of
   Symmetries                                          238
8. General Remarks About Groups of Symmetries
   of Second Order Ordinary Differential
   Equations                                           243
9. Lie's Problem from Cartan's Exterior Differential System Viewpoint                             245

Page

Chapter E:   THE GALOIS-PICARD-VESSIOT THEORY OF
             LINEAR ORDINARY DIFFERENTIAL EQUATIONS        247

   1. Introduction                                         247
   2. The Lie-Vessiot Form of a Linear Ordinary
      Scalar Differential Equation                         248
   3. The Galois Group According to the Ideas of
      Lie and Vessiot
   4. A Galois Theory for a Linear First Order
      Partial Differential Operator                        263

BIBLIOGRAPHY                                               271

Chapter A

## CONTACT MANIFOLDS AND MAPPING
## ELEMENT SPACES

### 1.    INTRODUCTION

The basic geometric idea in Lie's work on differential equations and differential invariants involves the
construction of what we would now call "functors from
categories of manifolds to categories of differential
fiber spaces".  Ehresmann's Theory of Jets is a close
approximation, in terms of modern manifold theory, to the
general concepts that Lie had in mind.  In this preliminary chapter I will develop independently the material
and notions that are needed to understand Lie's work in
the paper to be translated below.

In my previous books, particularly  LAQM, VB and
GPS, I have developed the geometric and physical ramifications of the Ehresmann "jet" ideas.  In order to keep
closer to the terminology and ideas of the 19th century
work, I now propose some changes in terminology and
notation.  For example, the "space of r-th order jets of
mappings from the manifold  X  to the manifold  Z,  denoted
by  $J^r(X,Z)$", now becomes the "space of r-th order <u>mapping
elements</u> of maps from  X  to  Z,  denoted by  $M^r(X,Z)$".

I will also guide the development of the theory towards
Cartan's general ideas concerning the geometry of mappings
and submanifolds, as briefly sketched in his paper "Sur
le problème général de la déformation", Oeuvres, Part III,
Vol. 1, p. 539, and developed further in my paper "Equivalence invariants for submanifolds of homogeneous spaces",
Math. Ann. 158, 284-289 (1965) and in GPS.

In this work, manifolds will typically be denoted by

$$X, Y, Z \quad .$$

A typical point of $X$ is denoted by $x$. A <u>coordinate
system</u> for $X$ is denoted by

$$(x^i) , \qquad 1 \leq i, j \leq n = \dim X \quad .$$

2.      MAPPINGS WHICH AGREE TO THE r-TH ORDER

Let $X, Z$ be manifolds. (All manifolds, maps, tensor-
fields, etc. will be of differentiability class $C^\infty$ unless
mentioned otherwise.)

$$M(X, Z)$$

denotes the space of mappings

$$\phi: X \to Z \quad .$$

<u>Notational Remarks</u>.  Later on, I will often denote elements
of  M(X,Z)  by

$$\underline{z} \ .$$

The reader will no doubt be familiar from calculus with
the utility (particularly for calculation) of denoting a
mapping in this way, by the letter assigned to the dependent variables.  (Physicists and chemists, especially, like
to do this, e.g., in <u>thermodynamics</u>.)  This notation can
lead to notational confusion, and this device of using the
dependent variable <u>underlined</u> might resolve some of the
confusion.  Of course, the weakness of notation of this
type inevitably shows up when changes are made in the
independent variable space  X.

<u>Definition</u>.  Let  $\phi,\phi' \in M(X,Z)$  and let  x  be a point
of  X.  Let  r  be a non-negative integer  $\phi$  and  $\phi'$
are said to <u>agree to the r-th order at</u>  x  if the following condition is satisfied:

> For each  $f \in F(Z)$,  each curve  $t \to x(t)$
> in  X  which starts at  x  for  t = 0,

$$f(\phi(x)) \ = \ f(\phi'(x))$$

$$\frac{d}{dt} \ (f(\phi(x(t))) \ - \ f(\phi'(x(t))))|_{t=0} \ = \ 0$$
$$\vdots$$
$$\frac{d^r}{dt^r} \ (f(\phi(x(t))) \ - \ f(\phi'(x(t))))|_{t=0} \ = \ 0$$

(2.1)

<u>Remarks</u>. a) If $X = R^n$, and $Z$ is a vector space,
(2.1) means that:

$$\phi(x) = \phi'(x)$$

$$\frac{\partial \phi}{\partial x^i}(x) = \frac{\partial \phi'}{\partial x^i}(x)$$

$$\vdots \qquad\qquad\qquad\qquad (2.2)$$

$$\frac{\partial^r \phi}{\partial x^{i_1} \ldots \partial x^{i_r}}(x) = \frac{\partial \phi'}{\partial x^{i_1} \ldots \partial x^{i_r}}(x)$$

i.e., all partial derivatives up to order r agree at  x.

   b)  If  X  is a manifold, and if  Z  is a vector
space, we can rephrase the condition as follows:

$$D(\phi)(x) = D(\phi')(x) \qquad\qquad (2.3)$$

for all linear differential operators

$$D: M(X,Z) \to F(X)(\equiv M(X,R))$$

of order at most r.  (See GPS, Chapter I for an algebraic,
intrinsic definition of differential operators.)

   c)  The definition can be put into an equivalent,
and often convenient form, using the notion of <u>higher</u>
order tangent spaces to a manifold (in the sense of Pohl).

See GPS, Chapter 3, Section 13.  For  $x \in X$,  let

$$X_x^r$$

denote this higher order tangent space.  Explicitly,  $X_x^r$
consists of the R-linear maps

$$v: F(M) \to R$$

such that there is an r-th order linear differential
operator  $D: F(M) \to F(M)$  with:

$$v(f) = D(f)(x)$$

$$\text{for all } f \in F(M) .$$

In words,  $X_x^r$  consists of the <u>values at</u>  x  of the r-th
order scalar, linear differential operators on  X.

Each map

$$\phi: X \to Z$$

defines a "prolongation" map

$$\phi_*: X_x^r \to Z_{\phi(x)}^r$$

via the following formula:

$$\phi_*(v)(f) = v(\phi^*(f))$$

$$\text{for all } v \in X_x^r, \quad f \in F(Z) .$$

Now, we can say that maps

$$\phi, \phi': X \to Z$$

agree to the r-<u>th order at</u>  x  if:

$$\phi(x) \;=\; \phi'(x)$$

$$\phi_*(v) \;=\; \phi'_*(v)$$

for all  $v \in X_x^r$  .

It would be convenient to be able to operate algebraically as freely with "differentials" as mathematicians did in the 19-th century.  I will now sketch a way of doing this for the case of <u>mappings between vector spaces</u>.

3.    A MULTILINEAR ALGEBRAIC FORMULA FOR DIFFERENTIALS OF MAPS BETWEEN VECTOR SPACES

Let  X  and  Z  be <u>vector spaces</u>, and let

$$\phi: X \to Z$$

be a mapping with domain  X  and range  Z.  (We suppose the domain is all of  X  only for notational convenience. It would be possible to modify things to cover the case where the domain of  $\phi$  is an open subset of  X.)

x  denotes a vector of  X.  Let

dx

denote another vector of  X.  Hence

$$x + dx$$

is an element of  X.

Write the <u>Taylor series</u> for  $\phi$  as follows:

$$\phi(x+dx) = \phi(x) + d\phi(x)(dx)$$

$$+ \frac{1}{2!} d^2\phi(x)(dx \circ dx)$$

(3.1)

$$+ \frac{1}{3!} d^3\phi(x)(dx \circ dx \circ dx)$$

$$+ \cdots$$

Here is the interpretation of what these terms mean.
For fixed  x,

$$dx \rightarrow d\phi(x)(dx)$$

is a linear map  $: X \rightarrow Z$. We denote this space of linear
maps by

$$L(X,Z)$$

(See Volumes I, II and VIII for standard algebraic terminology.)  Thus,  $d\phi$,  the <u>first order differential</u> of
$\phi$,  is a map

$$d\phi: X \rightarrow L(X,Z) \quad \cdot$$

The <u>second order differential</u>,  $d^2\phi$,  is a map

$$d^2\phi: X \rightarrow L(X \circ X, Z)$$

$X \circ X$ denotes the <u>symmetric tensor product of</u> $X$ <u>with
itself</u>. (See Volume II of IM.) Similarly, for $r = 3,4,\ldots$

$$d^r \phi : X \to \underbrace{L(X \cdots X, Z)}_{r \text{ factors}}$$

is called the r-<u>th order differential of</u> $\phi$.

In terms of this concept we can restate the condition described in Section 2.

<u>Definition</u>. Let $\phi, \phi'$ be maps $X \to Z$ between vector
spaces. $\phi$ and $\phi'$ are said to <u>agree to the</u> r-<u>th order
at</u> $x \in X$ if the following conditions are satisfied:

$$\phi(x) = \phi'(x)$$

$$d\phi(x) = d\phi'(x) \qquad\qquad (3.2)$$

$$\vdots$$

$$d^r \phi(x) = d^r \phi'(x)$$

Another way of putting this is to say that the
Taylor series for the map

$$dx \to \phi(x+dx) - \phi'(x+dx)$$

about the point $dx = 0$ has only non-vanishing terms
of order $\geq r+1$.

4.    MAPPING ELEMENT SPACES

Return to the general manifold situation.  Let  X
and  Z  be manifolds.  Denote the space of  $C^\infty$  maps

$$\phi: X \to Z$$

by

$$M(X,Z) \quad .$$

For each non-negative integer  r  introduces an
equivalence relation into  $X \times M(X,Z)$  as follows:

$(x,\phi)$  is equivalent to  $(x',\phi')$

if the following conditions are

satisfied:

$x = x'$

$\phi$  and  $\phi'$  agree to order r                    (4.1)

at  $x = x'$

The quotient of  $X \times M(X,Z)$  by this equivalence relation
is denoted by

$$M^r(X,Z) \quad ,$$

and is called the r-th order mapping element space.

If  $(x,\phi) \ \varepsilon \ X \times M(X,Z),$  denote the equivalence
class to which  $(x,\phi)$  belongs by

$$\partial^r \phi(x) \ \varepsilon \ M^r(X,Z) \quad .$$

As x varies over X, we obtain a map

$$x \rightarrow \partial^r \phi(x)$$

of

$$X \rightarrow M^r(X,Z)$$

called the r-th prolongation of φ.

Remark. If X and Z are vector spaces,

$$\partial^r \phi(x) = \partial^r \phi'(x)$$

if and only if

$$d^j \phi(x) = d^j \phi'(x)$$

$$\text{for } j = 0,1,2,\ldots,r \quad.$$

The reader must be careful to understand that $\partial^r$ stands
for all derivatives up to and including those of order r,
while $d^r \phi$ involves those of precisely order r.

In the Ehresmann notation,

$$M^r(X,Z) \equiv J^r(X,Z)$$

$$\partial^r \phi = j^r(\phi) \quad.$$

I have changed the terminology from "jets" to "mapping
element spaces" because I believe it is less confusing
to those who must use mathematics, and because it is
closer to the 19-th century terminology. In particular,
Lie introduced these spaces in all but name, and much of

his work on the connection between group theory and differential equations involves their study.

$M^r(X,Z)$ has a <u>Pfaffian system</u> P intrinsically defined on it. (See Volume IX of IM. A "Pfaffian system" on a manifold W is a $F(W)$-submanifold of $F^1(W)$, the one-differential forms on W.) This system has the following property:

$$(\partial^r \phi)*(P) = 0 \qquad (4.2)$$

$$\text{for each} \quad \phi \; \varepsilon \; M(X,Z) \quad .$$

The definition of P in terms of local coordinates for X and Z is described in detail in GPS, Chapter 3.

<u>Example</u>.   $X = Z = R$

$M^r(X,Z)$ then has coordinates

$$(x,z,z',z'',\ldots,z^{(r)})$$

such that:

For $\phi: X \to Z$ defined in coordinates $(x,z)$ by $x \to z(x)$,

$$j^r(\phi)*(x) = x$$

$$j^r(\phi)*(z) = z(x)$$

$$j^r(\phi)(z') = \frac{dz}{dx}(x)$$

$$\vdots$$

$$j^r(\phi)(z^{(r)}) = \frac{d^r z}{dx^r}(x)$$

$$(4.3)$$

Then,  P  has as basis the following one-forms:

$$\theta_1 = dz - z'dx$$

$$\theta_2 = dz' - z''dx$$

$$\vdots$$

$$\theta_{r-1} = dz^{(r-1)} - z^{(r)}dx$$

(4.4)

Terminology.  P  is called the <u>contact system</u>.


## 5.    DIFFERENTIABLE SUBSETS OF MANIFOLDS

We now briefly describe some material that will be useful in the next sections for defining "differential equations". Let  W  be a manifold.

<u>Definition</u>.  A set of real-valued functions  $f_1,\ldots,f_m \in F(W)$ on  W  are said to be <u>functionally independent</u> if the set of points of  W  at which their differentials

$$df_1,\ldots,df_m$$

are linearly independent forms an  <u>open</u>, <u>dense</u> subsets of  W.

<u>Example</u>.  Suppose  m = 1.  Consider a point at which $df_1 = 0$.  The above condition requires that there be points arbitrarily close at which  $df_1 \neq 0$.  If it is <u>not</u> satisfied, there will be open <u>subsets</u> of  W  at all of whose points

$$df_1 = 0 \quad ,$$

i.e., $f_1$ = constant. Thus, a single function $f_1$ is functionally independent if and only if there is not an open subset of M on which $f_1$ is constant.

Definition. A subset $W' \subset W$ is said to be a differential variety of W if there is at least one functionally independent set $(f_1, \ldots, f_m)$ of functions such that:

$$W' = \{w \epsilon W: f_1(w) = 0 = \cdots = f_m(w)\}$$

Remark. I have patterned the definition of "differential variety" after the definition of "algebraic variety". (See Volume VIII of IM.)

6.    DIFFERENTIAL EQUATIONS AND CONTACT TRANSFORMATIONS

Let X and Z be manifolds. Let $M^r(X,Z)$ be the r-th order mapping element space. It is also a manifold. Let $P \subset F^1(M^r(X,Z))$ be the contact Pfaffian system.

Definition. An r-th order system of differential equations, with X as independent variable manifold, Z as dependent variable manifold, is defined as a differential subset

$$DE(X,Z) \subset M^r(X,Z) \quad .$$

A map $\phi: X \to Z$ is a <u>solution</u> of the system if

$$\partial^r \phi(X) \subset DE(X,Z) \tag{6.1}$$

<u>Definition</u>. An <u>r-th order contact transformation</u> is defined as a pair $(U,U')$ of open subsets of $M^r(X,Z)$, and a diffeomorphism

$$\phi: U \to U'$$

such that

$$\phi^*(P) = P . \tag{6.2}$$

If DE, (DE)' are differential equation systems with X as independent variable manifold, Z as dependent variable manifold, a contact transformation

$$\phi: U \to U''$$

is said to <u>transform</u> DE <u>into</u> (DE)' if it satisfies the following condition:

$$\phi((DE) \cap U) \subset (DE)' \cap U' \tag{6.3}$$


7.    CONTACT ELEMENT SPACES

A key geometric idea in the 19-th century work on differential equations is to relate differential equation properties of maps $\phi: X \to Z$ to properties of the <u>graph</u>

of such a map

$$gr(\phi): X \to X \times Z \quad .$$

Now, $gr(\phi)$ is the map

$$x \to (x, \phi(x)) \quad . \tag{7.1}$$

It defines $X$ as a submanifold of $X \times Z$. In this section
I present some basic differential geometric material
concerning submanifolds, and the relation to graphs of
mappings.

Let $X$ and $W$ be manifolds. A map

$$\alpha: X \to W$$

is a submanifold map if

$$\alpha_*: T(X) \to T(W)$$

is one-one. ($T(X)$ denotes the tangent vector bundle to
$X$. $\alpha_*$ denotes the linear map $\phi$ defines on tangent
vectors.)

Let

$$SM(X,W)$$

denote the space of submanifold maps $\alpha: X \to W$, with $X$
fixed. Let

$$SM(W)$$

denote the space of submanifolds

$$\alpha: X \to W \quad ,$$

with the parameter manifold  X  <u>not</u> fixed.

<u>Definition</u>.  Let

$$\alpha: X \rightarrow W$$

$$\alpha': X' \rightarrow W$$

be two submanifold maps.  Let  $x \in X$,  $x' \in X'$  be points
such that:

$$\alpha(x) \ = \ \alpha'(x') \tag{7.2}$$

i.e.,  $\alpha(X)$  and  $\alpha'(X')$  meet at the point  $\alpha(x) \in W$.

<u>Definition</u>.  The submanifolds  $\alpha, \alpha'$  <u>meet to the</u> r-<u>th</u>
<u>order</u> at the point  $\alpha(x)$  if (7.2) is satisfied, and in
addition the following condition is satisfied:

There are open subsets

$$x \in U \subset X$$

$$x' \in U' \subset X'$$

and a diffeomorphism

$$\beta: U \rightarrow U'$$

such that

$$\beta(x) \ = \ x'$$

$\alpha$  and  $\alpha\beta'$,  as maps  $U \rightarrow W$,
agree to the r-th order at  x.

Definition. Let   r   and   n   be positive integers, and
let  w ε W.  Consider the space of  m  dimensional submanifolds of  W  which pass through the point  w.   Let
us say that two of them are equivalent if they intersect
to r-th order at  w.   Denote the set of these equivalence
classes by

$$C^r(W,n)(w) \quad .$$

Let

$$C^r(W,n)$$

denote the space of ordered pairs

$$(w,\gamma) \quad ,$$

where  w ε W,   $\gamma$ ε $C^r(W,n)(w)$  .

$C^r(W,n)$  is called the space of r-th order, n-dimensional
contact elements of the manifold  W.

Map

$$C^r(W,n) \to W$$

by assigning

$$(w,\gamma) \to w \quad .$$

This defines  $C^r(W,n)$  as a fiber space over  W.

Special Case.  r = 1

$C^1(W,n)$ = Grassman bundle of n-dimensional linear
subspaces of  T(W).

To see this, let

$$\alpha: X \to W \quad,$$

$$\alpha': X' \to W$$

be n-dimensional submanifolds, with

$$\alpha(x) = \alpha'(x') = w$$

Suppose first that they intersect to first order. Then, there is a diffeomorphism

$$\beta: X \to X'$$

(which may be only "locally defined" about x) such that:

$$\beta(x) = x'$$

$$(\alpha'\beta)_* = \alpha_*: X_x \to W_w \quad.$$

But,

$$(\alpha'\beta)_* = \alpha'_*\beta_* = \alpha_* \quad.$$

This means that:

$$\alpha_*(X_x) = \alpha'_*(X_{x'}) \quad.$$

<u>If</u> $\alpha$ <u>and</u> $\alpha'$ <u>intersect to the first order at</u> w, <u>then</u> <u>they map the tangent space to</u> X <u>at</u> x <u>into the same</u> n-<u>dimensional linear subspace of</u> $X_x$.

Conversely, suppose $\alpha$ and $\alpha'$ satisfy this condition. It follows from linear algebra that there is a <u>linear map isomorphism</u> $\beta_*: X_x \to X'_{x'}$, such that:

$$\alpha_*^! \beta_* = \alpha_* \quad .$$

One can now construct $\beta$ as any diffeomorphism between X and X', carrying x into x', whose differential at x is $\beta_*$, and we see that it realizes the first order equivalence between $\alpha$ and $\alpha'$.

8. THE MAPPING ELEMENT SPACES AS OPEN SUBSETS OF THE CONTACT SPACES

Now, let X,Z be manifolds, and let

$$M^r(X,Z)$$

be the r-th order mapping elements of maps

$$\phi: X \to Z \quad .$$

Let:

$$W = X \times Z \quad .$$

We now show that there is a one-one map

$$\text{graph}: M^r(X,Z) \to C^r(W,n) \quad ,$$

whose image is an open subset of $C^r(W,n)$.

To this end, let

$$M(X,Z)$$

denote the space of all maps $X \to Z$. Let

$$SM(X,W \equiv X \times Z)$$

denote the space of all submanifold maps

$$\alpha\colon X \to X \times Z \ .$$

Here is the basic construction:  If

$$\phi \in M(X,Z) \ ,$$

let

$$\mathrm{graph}(\phi)\colon X \to X \times Z$$

be the map defined by the following formula:

$$(\mathrm{graph}\ \phi)(x) \ = \ (x,\phi(x)) \tag{8.1}$$

This should be familiar to the reader from calculus,
e.g., in the case

$$X \ = \ Z \ = \ R$$

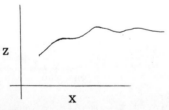

Notice that  graph $\phi$  is a <u>submanifold</u> of  $X \times Z$.  However,
not every submanifold map  $\alpha\colon X \to X \times Z$  arises from a
graph.

<u>Theorem 8.1</u>.  Let  $\alpha\colon X \to X \times Z$  be a submanifold map,
and let

$$\pi\colon X \times Z \to X$$

be the Cartesian projection. Then, $\alpha$ can, <u>after a</u>
<u>change in parameterization</u>, arise as the graph of a map
$\phi: X \rightarrow Z$ if and only if the following condition is
satisfied:

$$\pi\phi: X \rightarrow X \quad \text{is a diffeomorphism} \qquad (8.2)$$

    <u>Proof</u>. Suppose first that $\alpha$ can be reparameter-
ized to be a graph. This means that there is a diffeomorphism

$$\beta: X \rightarrow X$$

and a map $\phi: X \rightarrow Z$ such that:

$$\alpha(\beta(x)) = (x, \phi(x)) \quad .$$

Then,

$$\alpha(x) = (\beta^{-1}(x), \phi(\beta^{-1}(x)))$$

Thus,

$$\pi\alpha(x) = \beta^{-1}(x) \quad , \quad \text{i.e.,}$$

$$\pi\alpha = \beta^{-1}, \quad \text{a diffeomorphism} \quad .$$

We have shown that condition (8.2) is necessary. The
steps in the proof are reversible to show that it is also
sufficient.

    Here is a way of formalizing this property.

<u>Definition</u>. A submanifold map

$\alpha: X \to X \times Z$

is said to be <u>transversal to</u> X if

$\pi\alpha: X \to X$

is a diffeomorphism.

<u>Remark</u>. In certain circumstances, one might want to weaken condition (8.2) by requiring that $\pi\alpha$ is a <u>local diffeomorphism</u>. This corresponds to requiring that $\alpha$ can <u>locally</u> be reparameterized to be a graph. In case

$X = Z = R$

these conditions should be familiar from calculus. The first curve in $W = R^2$ satisfies the condition, the second does not, because its <u>tangent vector becomes vertical</u>.

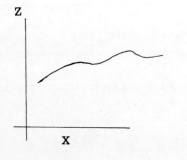 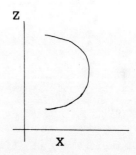

Thus, "graph" defines a mapping

$$M(X,Z) \rightarrow SM(X,Z) \quad .$$

This map will induce a map

$$\overline{gr}: M^r(X,Z) \rightarrow C^r(M,n) \quad . \tag{8.2}$$

To see how the map is defined, here is the basic fact:

Theorem 8.2. Let $\phi, \phi': X \rightarrow Z$ be maps, such that

$$\phi(x) = \phi'(x')$$

$$w = (x, \phi(x)) \in X \times Z \quad .$$

Then, $graph(\phi)$ and $graph(\phi')$ intersect to the r-th order at $w$ if and only if $\phi$ and $\phi'$ agree to the r-th order at $x$.

Proof. Suppose first that $graph(\phi)$ and $graph(\phi')$ intersect to the r-th order. This means that there is a diffeomorphism $\beta: X \rightarrow X$ with

$$\beta(x) = x'$$

and such that:

$$x \rightarrow (\beta(x), \phi(\beta(x)))$$

and

$$x \rightarrow (x, \phi'(x))$$

agree to the r-th order at the point $x$. This requires that:

$$\beta(x) = x \; . \tag{8.3}$$

$$\beta_* : X_x^r \to X_r^r \tag{8.4}$$

is the _identity_ map.

$$(\phi\beta)_* : X_x^r \to Z_{\phi(x)}^r$$

and

$$(\phi')_* : X_x^r \to Z_{\phi(x)}^r$$

_agree_. But,

$$(\phi\beta)_* = \phi_*\beta_* = \text{,using (8.4), } \phi_* \; ,$$

hence

$$\phi_* = \phi'_* \; ,$$

which means that $\phi$ and $\phi'$ agree to the r-th order at $x$. Conversely, if this condition is satisfied the steps are reversible.

Now, let

$$\overline{gr} : M^r(X,Z) \to C^r(X \times Z, n) \tag{8.5}$$

be the map which results from passing to the quotient, using the knowledge provided by Theorem 8.2 that _graph_ preserves the equivalence relation defining these two spaces. Theorem 8.2 also proves that $\overline{gr}$ is one-one.

_Remark_. So far, we have not defined any topology or manifold structure for $M^r(X,Z)$ or $C^r(X \times Z, n)$. At this point it would be appropriate, but I will sketch what is involved.

Local coordinates for X and Z define coordinates for $M^r(X,Z)$, since the partial derivatives "pass to the quotient". Define the topology and manifold structure for $M^r(X,Z)$ using these local coordinates.

Now, define the topology and manifold structure for $C^r(W,n)$ by requiring that the images

$$\overline{gr}(M^r(X,Z))$$

be open submanifolds whenever the manifold W is written as a Cartesian product $W = X \times Z$, with dim X = n.


9. PROLONGATION OF GROUP AND LIE ALGEBRA ACTIONS

Now we come to the key geometric element in Lie's work on the connection between group theory and differential equations. Let W be a manifold of dimension greater than n, and let

$$C^r(W,n)$$

be the manifold of n-dimensional, r-th order contact elements. Let

$$g: W \to W$$

be a diffeomorphism of W.

g   acts on

SM(W)   ,

in the natural geometric way, i.e.,

if   $\alpha$: X $\to$ W   is a submanifold map,

then   g$\alpha$   is the composite map

x $\to$ g($\alpha$(x))   .

g,   acting in this way on   SM(W),   passes to the quotient
(i.e., preserves the geometric property of "intersecting
to the r-th order") and hence acts on

$C^r$(W,n)   .

We denote the map obtained on   $C^r$(W,n)   in this way by

$g^r$: $C^r$(W,n) $\to$ $C^r$(W,n)   .

If   G   is a <u>group</u> of diffeomorphisms of   W,   it is
obvious that the map

g $\to$ $g^r$

is a group homomorphism, and that it is one-one.  This
defines an action of   G   on   $C^r$(W,n)   that is called the
r-<u>th order prolongation of</u>   G.

There is also a prolongation map at the Lie algebra
level.  If

A $\varepsilon$ V(W)

is a vector field, let us suppose that it is the infinitesimal generator of a one-parameter group of diffeomorphisms

$$t \to g(t)$$

W.  (In general, it will only generate a local group, but,
with a little more notational difficulty this would work
just as well.)  Then

$$t \to g(t)^r$$

is a one-parameter group of diffeomorphisms of $C^r(W,n)$.
Denote its infinitesimal generator by

$$A^r.$$

The map

$$A \to A^r$$

of

$$V(W) \to V(C^r(W,n))$$

is called the r-th order prolongation on vector fields.
It preserves Jacobi brackets, i.e., is a Lie algebra homomorphism.

In particular, this may be applied to the case where

$$W = X \times Z .$$

Groups acting on  W  may be prolonged to act on  $C^r(W,n)$,
which contains  $M^r(X,Z)$  as an open, dense subset.  Vector
fields may be prolonged, defining a Lie algebra homomorphism

$$V(X \times Z) \quad \rightarrow \quad V(M^r(X,Z))$$

Let

$$P \subset F^1(M^r(X,Z))$$

be the Pfaffian system defined by the mapping elements.
Given

$$g: X \times Z \rightarrow X \times Z \quad ,$$

its prolongation $g^r$ satisfies

$$(g^r)^*(P) \quad = \quad P \quad ,$$

i.e., is a "symmetry" of P. Similarly, if

$$A \in V(X \times Z),$$

$$A^r(P) \subset P \quad .$$

In practice this property (together with the relation

$$\pi_*(A^r) \quad = \quad A \quad ,$$

where

$$\pi: M^r(X,Z) \rightarrow X \times Z$$

is the natural projection map) gives a convenient way to
calculate $A^r$.

In summary, in this preliminary chapter I have given
an outline of the modern way of development of the basic
geometric concepts that Lie uses in this paper. Let us
now turn to the paper itself, where we will have the
chance to see many examples and applications.

# ON DIFFERENTIAL INVARIANTS

Math Ann. Vol. XXIV, No. 4, pp. 537-578
[Collected Papers, Vol. VI, pp. 95-138]

by Sophus Lie

In this brief paper I consider mainly <u>continuous</u> <u>transformation groups with infinitely many parameters</u> and <u>sketch</u> a general <u>invariant theory</u> of these, whose main theorem I have communicated to the <u>Gesellschaft der Wissen-</u> <u>schaften</u> in Christiania in 1883 [Collected Papers, Vol. II, paper XKI, p. 559, No. V].

At the same time I summarize some older investigations of continuous groups with a finite number of parameters and add some remarks, in part general and in part personal, on the relations of my many years' work on differential equa- tions to the investigations of other researchers. If my citations are incomplete, which is to be feared, I will make corrections in later publications.

Although I shall cite my own previous works quite frequently in the following, aside from the general theory of first-order (linear) partial differential equations and the concept of a contact transformation, the reader need only know the elements of my theory of transformation groups (Math. Ann. Vol. XVI, Volume 1 of "Lie Groups: History, Frontiers and Applications") to be able to understand the following work.

29

Chapter 1

INTRODUCTORY REMARKS


1.1     Even in my first investigations of differential

equations, which go back to 1869-72, the fundamental princi-

ple was a consistent application of the theory of point and

contact-transformations.  I tried to develop a general trans-

formation theory and apply it to the theory of differential

equations.  On the one hand I sought criteria for the exis-

tence of a transformation bringing a given differential

equation or other analytic expression into a given form,

and on the other hand, I tried to find such transformations,

when they exist.

My first step along this path was the rational founda-

tion of the concept of a contact-transformation, and the

second was the fundamental introduction of the concept of

an infinitesimal transformation.  My first intention was the

foundation of an invariant theory of contact-transformations,

i.e., the study of those properties of differential equations

which are unchanged by all contact-transformations (or all

point-transformations).  In this direction I gave a rational

foundation of the general theory of first-order partial

differential equations.[*]  A further step in carrying out

[*] See the Abhandlungen der Gesellschaft der Wissenschaften
zu Christiania 1871, 1872, 1873, 1874 and 1875, and Math.
Ann. Vol. VIII (Bergründung einer Invariantentheorie der
Berührungstransformationen (Foundations of an invariant theory
of contact transformations) 1874, Vol. I, papers XI, XII;
Vol. III, papers I, II, V-X, XII, XV, XVI; Vol. IV, papers I-
III; Vol. III, papers III, IV].

my general program was the <u>foundation of a general theory</u>
<u>of continuous transformation groups with a finite number of</u>
<u>parameters and a general application of this concept to the</u>
<u>theory of differential equations</u>.

My investigations of those groups which may be called
<u>finite continuous groups</u> have been published for the most
part in Norwegian journals (partly also in Gött. Nachr.,
Dec. 1874, in Math. Ann. Vol. XI, p. 487 and Vol. XVI [Col-
lected Papers Vol. V, paper I; Vol. IV, paper III, Section II;
Vol. VI, paper I], and I hope soon to present them to a
larger public in a complete way.

Finally, I have recently[*] developed the first principles of a general <u>theory of continuous groups with infinitely</u>
<u>many parameters</u>.  It turns out that one can put all these
groups, which may be called <u>infinite continuous groups</u> into
simple canonical forms.  In the general study of differential equations the infinite continuous groups will also play
a fundamental role.


1.2     DIFFERENTIAL INVARIANTS

If the quantities $x_1,\ldots,x_n$, $z_1,\ldots,z_q$ are connected
with the new variables $x_1',\ldots,x_n'$, $z_1',\ldots,z_q'$ by transformation equations which form a group, where $z_1,\ldots,z_q$ are

---

[*] Ges. d. Wiss. zu Christiania 1883, No. 12 [Collected
Papers Vol. V, paper XIII.]

functions of $x_1,\ldots,x_n$ and $z_1',\ldots,z_q'$ are functions of $x_1',\ldots,x_n'$, then the $\partial z_i/\partial x_k$ are functions of the $x_k',z_i'$ and the $\partial z_i'/\partial x_k'$. With these hypotheses I call a function of the form

$$\Omega\left(x_1,\ldots,x_n,\ z_1,\ldots,z_q,\ \frac{\partial z_1}{\partial x_1}\ ,\ldots,\ \frac{\partial^2 z_i}{\partial x_k \partial x_m}\ ,\ldots\right)$$

a <u>differential invariant of the group</u> if

$$\Omega\left(x_1,\ldots,z_q,\ \frac{\partial z_1}{\partial x_1}\ ,\ldots,\ \frac{\partial^2 z_i}{\partial x_k \partial x_m}\ ,\ldots\right)$$

$$=\ \Omega\left(x_1',\ldots,z_q',\ \frac{\partial z_1'}{\partial x_1'}\ ,\ldots,\ \frac{\partial^2 z_i'}{\partial x_k' \partial x_m'}\ ,\ldots\right)$$

In this note I establish a general theorem, special cases of which have appeared before. It can be formulated as follows:

<u>Every infinite</u> (<u>and finite</u>) <u>continuous group deter-mines infinitely many differential invariants, which can be defined as the solutions of a complete system.</u>

For groups with a finite number of parameters this theorem is so-to-speak immediately evident. For this special case I have known it for a long time and touched upon it in 1872[*] and 1874 and on later occasions, I communicated it in

---

[*] Ges. d. Wiss. zu Christiania 1872: Zur Theorie der Differentialprobleme (On the theory of differential problems); Gött. Nachr., Dec. 1874 [Collected Papers Vol. III, paper V; Vol. V, paper I].

a more precise form to the Gesellschaft der Wissenschaften
in Christiania in July 1882 [Collected Papers Vol. V,
paper VIII, p. 236, No. 3].

    For groups with infinitely many parameters the above
theorem, which contains the deformation theory of surfaces
etc. of Gauss and his followers[*] as a special case, lies
somewhat deeper.  For a special case relating to the group
of all contact- or point-transformations, I pointed it out
in 1872 (Gött. Nachr. No. 25, pp. 478-479 [Collected Papers
Vol. III, paper IV, p. 19ff]).  That it extends to all
infinite continuous groups I explicitly communicated to the
Ges. d. Wiss. in Christiania in Nov. 1883 [Collected Papers
Vol. III, paper XLI, p. 559, No. V].

---

[*] I refer to the well-known investigations of Minding,
Beltrami, Christoffel, Lipschitz and Weingarten.  My theories
are also obviously related to the general invariant theory
of linear transformations due to Cayley, Sylvester, Aronhold,
Clebsch, Gordan, etc.

Chapter 2

## FUNCTIONS AND EQUATIONS WHICH ADMIT
## A FINITE CONTINUOUS GROUP

In this section I resume some older investigations
of functions of $x_1, \ldots, x_n$ which admit a finite continuous
group. At the same time I shall discuss thoroughly the
relations between my old investigations of this domain and
Klein's.

## 2.1    ORIGINS OF TRANSFORMATION GROUP THEORY

In investigations in 1869-70 of line-complexes whose
lines intersect a tetrahedron with constant cross-ratio, my
starting point was the remark that such a line system admits
an $\infty^3$ of commuting linear transformations.  I studied the
curves enveloped by complex-lines and also a large class of
contact transformations which take such curves into such
curves.

This connected with the investigation of a remarkable
second-order partial differential equation.  Its integral
surfaces are characterized by the fact that at each of their
points the principal tangents are in harmonic ratio with the
two tangents belonging to the complex.  This partial differential equation admits a very interesting group of contact-

transformations, whose properties I studied deeply.  I
integrated not only the second-order equation mentioned,
but also the first-order partial differential equation
which is a singular first integral of it.  The remarkable
new methods used in this turned out to be vastly general-
izable.

All these investigations,[*] which were scarcely
published, I explained to my contemporary student and friend
Felix Klein, who was then editing Plücker's Nachlass and had
been led by that to (among other things) interesting investigations of certain discontinuous projective groups which
play an important role in line-geometry.

Klein took a lively interest in my group-theoretic
studies, which differed from his mainly in that I considered
continuous and he discontinuous groups.  He energetically
encouraged me in my investigations and even took an active
part in them.  We published some joint notes on the curves
in the plane and space which admit infinitely many linear
transformations and also on the surfaces which admit an $\infty^2$

---

[*] I gave a resume of my results in Prof. Kummer's seminar in
the winter semester of 1869-70, and also in the Göttinger
Nachr. (Jan. 1870).  See also Ges. d. Wiss. in Christiania
1872 (Kurzes Resume...) and Archiv for Math. og Naturv.,
Christiania 1877, Vol. II (Synthetisch-analytische Untersuchungen über Minimalflächen [Synthetic-analytic investigations of minimal surfaces], §1) [Collected Papers Vol. I,
paper V; Vol. III, paper I and Vol. I, paper XVII, §1.]

of commuting linear transformations.[*]  It was our intention
to continue these important, if special investigations, but
our interests took other directions.

I discovered a remarkable contact transformation taking
straight lines into spheres and with one stroke thereby
transformed Plücker's line-geometry into a new sphere-geometry.
Among other things this yielded the fact that the group of all
projective transformations of space can be transformed to the
group of all contact transformations taking spheres into
spheres.[**]

---

[*] Sur une certaine famille de courbes et de surfaces par
F. Klein et S. Lie, Comptes Rendus 1870; Über diefenigen
ebenen Kurven..., Math. Ann. Vol. IV (1871). [Collected
Papers Vol. I, papers VI and XIV.]

[**] This group has recently acquired a new and heightened
interest through the discoveries of Stephanos in the quater-
mion calculus (Math. Ann. Vol. XXII, p. 589).

I take this opportunity to recall two old remarks of mine.
The group of sphere transformations mentioned in the text
can be considered as the group of all conformal point-
transformations of a four-dimensional space (Math. Ann. Vol. V,
p. 186, Gött. Nachr. 1871, pp. 207-208, 200-203 [Collected
Papers Vol. II, paper I, end of §13; Vol. I, paper XIII].
The group of all projective transformations of space leaving
invariant a given line can be transformed into the group of
all contact-transformations taking spheres into spheres and
parallel planes into parallel planes (Math. Ann. Vol. V,
p. 186; Gött. Nachr. 1871, p. 200). The latter group, to
which I gave special attention, has been recently studied
by Laguerre and Stephanos on the one hand and by Darboux on
the other. I had explicitly remarked that all surfaces with
the same spherical image are transformed into surfaces whose
new spherical image results from the old by a conformal transformation of the sphere.

*COMMENT*

*The material Lie alludes to here is extremely*
*fascinating and rich in ideas, but is unfortunately almost*
*completely lost to the modern reader.   The best reference*
*seems to be Lie and Scheffer's "Geometrie der Beruhrungs-*
*transformationen".   Darboux'  "Theorie des Surfaces",*
*Part I, also contains related material.*

*The transformation of "line geometry" into "sphere*
*geometry" is interesting, since it reflects the "accidental"*
*isomorphism of two elements of the families A and B of*
*simple Lie algebras.   (See Samelson [1]), namely:*

$$A_3 \quad \underline{is \ isomorphic \ to} \quad B_3.$$

*Here is a brief explanation of this point.*

*Let  L  be the space of all lines in  $C^3$, complex*
*Euclidean 3-space.   Let  S  be the space of all spheres*
*in  $C^3$.*

*SL(4,C)  is a Lie group whose Lie algebra is  $A_3$.*
*It acts--via <u>projective</u> transformation--in a <u>local</u>, <u>transi-</u>*
*<u>tive</u> way on  L.*

*SO(6,C)  is a Lie group, whose Lie algebra is  $B_3$.*
*Lie showed that  SO(6,C)  acts locally as <u>contact trans-</u>*
*<u>formations</u> on  $C^3$, with the property of taking spheres*
*into spheres. (The  SO(5,C) -subgroup acts as <u>conformal</u>*

*transformations.) Of course, this does not mean that*
$SO(6,C)$ *acts on* $C^3$ *itself, but on the* <u>*projective bundle*</u>
*associated with its cotangent bundle. It is a five-*
*dimensional space.*

*As contact transformations,* $SO(6,C)$ *acts in a*
<u>*locally transitive*</u> *way on S. Thus, Lie's equivalence*
*between S and L amounts, in modern terms, to showing*
*that two coset spaces, one of* $SL(4,C)$, *the other of*
$SO(6,C)$, *are isomorphic.*

*This correspondence has various remarkable properties*
*relative to the differential geometry of surfaces in* $C^3$
*and first and second order non-linear partial differential*
*equations in two independent and one dependent variable.*
*(For example, it enables one to set up transformations*
*which map surfaces into surfaces, in such a way that*
*"lines of principal curvature" go into "asymptotic lines".*
*This, in turn, is related to the theory of Bäcklund*
*Transformations, which has recently appeared in Applied*
*Mathematics, in terms of "soliton" solutions of non-*
*linear wave equations. See Witham [1].)*

*This material badly needs a modern exposition!*

Klein, on the other hand, developed comprehensive
geometrical and metaphysical ideas, especially in his
deep Erlangen program of 1872 (Math. Ann., Vol. 43, 1893,
p. 63. English translation by W. Haskell, Bull. New York
Math. Soc., Vol. 2, 1892, p. 215.) whose fundamental
significance was recognized in circles which widened with
each year. At this point I shall cite only one passage
(p. 40) from this paper, which describes a problem pro-
pounded by both of us:

"In considering a manifold on which a group acts we
[i.e., Klein and Lie] ask ... first of all ... for the
configurations which are invariant under all transformations of the group. But there are configurations invariant under some, but not all, transformations of the group..."

## 2.2   DIFFERENTIAL EQUATIONS OF INVARIANTS

The general analytic solution of this problem, which
presents no major difficulties to a synthetic conception,
is contained in some theories[*] developed by me in 1874,
which will be reproduced here in brief.

---

[*] See also Verhandlungen der Ges. d. Wiss. zu Christiania
1872:  Zur Theorie der Differentialprobleme (On the theory
of differential problems), p. 132 [Collected Papers, Vol. III,
paper V].

I denote an infinitesimal transformation of $x_1, \ldots, x_n$ under which these quantities receive the increments

$$\delta x_k = \xi_k(x_1, \ldots, x_n) \, \delta t \; {}^{*}$$

by the symbol

$$B = \xi_1 \frac{\partial}{\partial x_1} + \cdots + \xi_n \frac{\partial}{\partial x_n} \quad .$$

Thus, under this transformation the function $\Omega(x_1, \ldots, x_n)$ receives the increment $B(\Omega) \cdot \delta t$.

Hence $\Omega$ admits the infinitesimal transformation $B$ if $B\Omega$ vanishes identically. (Ges. d. Wiss. zu Christiania; Nov. 1874: Zur Theorie des Integrabilitätsfaktors (On the theory of the integrating factor) p. 244; Verallgemeinerung und neue Verwertung des Jacobischen Multiplikatortheorie (Generalization and new application of the theory of the Jacobi multiplier) p. 256; Math. Ann. Vol. XI, p. 535 [Collected Papers Vol. III, paper XIII, p. 177ff; paper XIV, p. 188ff; Vol. IV, paper III, §15, No. 38]).

An equation $\Phi = 0$ admits the infinitesimal trans-formation $B$ if the equation $B\Phi = 0$ is a consequence of $\Phi = 0$ alone. Likewise a system of equations

$$\Phi_1 = 0, \ldots, \Phi_q = 0$$

---

${}^{*}$ In the following it is assumed that the $\xi_k$ are analytic functions of the $x_k$.

admits the infinitesimal transformation  B  if all the  $B\Phi_k$
vanish as a consequence of  $\Phi_i = 0$.  One thus has the
following, which is a fundamental idea of my work:  the
search for the common solutions  $f_k$  of given partial
differential equations

$$B_1 f = 0, \; B_2 f = 0 \;,\ldots, \; B_r f = 0 \quad,$$

coincides with the determination of all functions which
admit the infinitesimal transformations  $B_k$.  Hence, <u>the
solution of the latter problem is to be found in the Jacobi-
Clebsh theory of complete systems</u>.

Hence, if  $B_1 f = 0,\ldots,B_q f = 0$  is a complete system
with solutions  $f_1,f_2,\ldots,f_{n-q}$,  then  $\Omega(f_1,f_2,\ldots,f_{n-q})$
is the general form of a function admitting the infinitesi-
mal transformation  $B_k$.

If an equation  $\Phi = 0$  satisfies the equations
$B_k\Phi = 0$  of our complete system, then in general it has the
form

$$\Phi(f_1,f_2,\ldots,f_{n-q}) \;=\; 0 \quad.$$

If this is not the case, then it is well-known that  $\Phi$  must
be of such a form that the independence of the equations
$B_k f = 0$  is contradicted by  $\Phi = 0$.  Hence one finds all
such equations  $\Phi = 0$  by forming determinants, bearing in
mind that in general one must verify afterwards that the

equations found in this way actually satisfy the relations
$B_k f = 0$. One finds the most general system of equations
$\Phi_k = 0$  satisfying  $B_i \Phi_k = 0$  in a similar way.

An r-parameter continuous group of transformations
of  $x_1,\ldots,x_n$  contains  $\infty^{r-1}$  infinitesimal transformations.
One can always choose  r  of these, say  $B_1,B_2,\ldots,B_r$,  of
which the others are linear combinations, so that their
general symbol is

$$c_1 B_1 + \cdots + c_r B_r \qquad\qquad (c_k = const.) \quad .$$

One has the characteristic relations*

$$[B_i,B_k] = \sum c_{iks} B_s \quad . \qquad\qquad (2.2.1)$$

Every finite transformation of the group is generated by an
infinite iteration of some infinitesimal transformation
$\sum^J c_k B_k$  of the group. Hence the functions  $\Omega$  or the
equations  $\Phi = 0$  which admit out group are again defined
by the equations

$$B_1 f = 0 ,\ldots, B_r f = 0 ,$$

which always determine a complete system

---

* In the Archiv for Math. og Naturv. Vol. I, pp. 178-181,
1876 [Collected Papers Vol. V, paper III, pp. 63-65] I
showed that all subgroups of a given group can be found
by algebraic operations, and moreover, that the discussion
can be reduced to <u>linear</u> groups.
    A proof of <u>my old</u> formula (2.2.1), which also plays
a fundamental role in this work, is given in <u>Theorem 4.12</u>.

$$B_1 f = 0 \ , \ldots, \ B_q f = 0 \qquad\qquad (q \leq r)$$

See Gött. Nachr. Dec. 1974;  Math. Ann. Vol. XVI, p. 462;
Archiv for Math. og Natur. Vol. I, pp. 163-165, 1876;
Vol. III, p. 118 at the beginning of the year 1878.  [Collected Papers Vol. V, paper I;  Vol. VI, paper I, p. 23ff.;
Vol. V, paper III, pp. 51-53;  paper IV, p. 97ff.]

In the last cited work I considered a completely
arbitrary group $B_1, \ldots, B_r$ and used its invariants, i.e.,
the solutions $f_1, \ldots, f_{n-q}$ of the complete system
$B_1 f = 0 \ , \ldots, \ B_q f = 0$ in treating a difficult problem
which I shall again take up in the next work[*] [Collected
Papers, Vol. VI, paper III, p. 165ff.].  See also my fourth
paper on transformation groups in my Archiv Vol. III, p. 379,
1878 [Collected Papers Vol. V, paper V, p. 138ff.].

---

[*] I shall assume that the equations $B_1 f = 0 \ , \ldots, \ B_r f = 0$
which generally reduce to $q \leq r$ equations, reduce to q-m
equations $B_k f = 0$ for those special values for which vanish
certain familiar determinants $\Phi_1, \Phi_2, \ldots, \Phi_s$. Then our group
leaves invariant the system of equations $\Phi_k = 0$ (Math.
Ann. Vol. XVI, pp. 474-478;  Archiv for Math. og Nature., 1883,
p. 195 [Collected Papers Vol. VI, paper I (Vol. XII of Interdisciplinary Mathematics), pp. 35-40;  Vol. V, paper X,
p. 245ff.].  If among the relations $\Phi_k = 0$ there are fewer
than n-q+m independent ones, then there are obviously invariant systems of equations containing certain equations in
addition to the relations $\Phi_k = 0$.  Hence if a system of
equations admits our group, then in general the system can
be expressed by means of some finite relations among the
invariants $f_k$ of the text.  If this is not possible, then
the system of equations contains a system $\Phi_k = 0$ of the
kind considered before;  under these conditions more easily
definable relations can occur.

Every finite transformation of the group $B_1, \ldots, B_r$ is gotten by an infinite iteration of an infinitesimal transformation $c_1 B_1 + \cdots + c_r B_r$, i.e., by integration of the linear partial differential equation

$$c_1 B_1 f + \cdots + c_r B_r f + \frac{\partial f}{\partial t} = 0$$

with arbitrary constants $c_1, \ldots, c_r$ (see e.g., Math. Ann. Vol. XVI, p. 464 [Collected Papers Vol. VI, paper I (Vol. XII of Interdisciplinary Mathematics), p. 25]). Hence if one knows the finite transformations of a given group, then finding the quantities $f_1, f_2, \ldots, f_{n-q}$ mentioned above requires only so-called permissible operations,[*] whose actual carrying out may, of course, present difficulties.

## 2.3    SURFACES WHICH ADMIT GROUPS

As already mentioned, in 1870 Klein and I had determined all surfaces which admit an $\infty^2$ of commuting linear transformations. In 1882 Poincaré (Journal de l'école polytechnique Vol. 31), whose works on discontinuous groups have been crowned with such brilliant success, dealt incidentally with the question of what surfaces admit several

---

[*] The conclusion in the text depends on the fact that a complete system $B_1 f = 0, \ldots, B_q f = 0$ can be integrated if each of the $q$ equations $B_i f = 0$ has been integrated.

linear transformations and solved this problem under certain

restrictive hypotheses.

Some months later I gave,[*] if I'm not mistaken, a

complete determination of all ruled surfaces which admit

linear groups.  The main point for me was the question,

which Poincaré didn't touch, of what linear groups are

defined by the property of leaving invariant a surface

(or a curve).[**]  In a later work (Comptes Rendus 1883)

Poincaré made similar investigations of n-dimensional space.

Here I recall also some very noteworthy investiga-

tions, sketched by Picard, of ordinary linear differential

-------

[*]   Archiv for Math. og Naturv. 1882, pp. 179-193 [Collected
Papers Vol. V, paper VII, pp. 224-234].  In a concluding
remark [loc. cit. o. 234] I added some general observations
on arbitrary groups and their differential invariants.
These are made precise in a passage from my note of 1872,
Zur Theorie der Differentialprobleme (On the theory of
differential problems), Ges. d. Wiss. zu Christiania 1872,
p. 132 [Collected Papers Vol. III, paper V] which is cited
in the next section [§ 3.1].

   Note that the Cayley line-surface of 3-rd order is
the only non-developable ruled surface of second degree
which admits more than two infinitesimal linear transformations.  Cayley's ruled surface, in addition to the two
commuting infinitesimal transformations discovered by Klein
and me, has a third such transformation.  It is well-known
that second-degree surfaces admit six such transformations.

[**] For the purposes of line- and sphere-geometry it is
interesting to note that the line and sphere are the only
figures in space which assume exactly $\infty^4$ positions under
all motions and similarity transformations.  Thus Plücker's
line-geometry and my sphere-geometry have a distinguished
position by the nature of things.

equations, which relate to a discussion of the subgroups of
the general projective group of an n-dimensional manifold
(Comptes Rendus 1883).

*COMMENTS*

*For an excellent review (without proofs) of this
material, as it stood in 1915 (and much else that is of
great interest for understanding Lie's work) see the
"Encyclopédie des Sciences Mathématiques" article, "La
théorie des groupes continues et la géométrie", by G. Fano
and E. Cartan. It is most conveniently to be found reprinted in Part III, Vol. 2 of Cartan's Collected Works.*

*The reference to Picard's work is what later became
known as Picard-Vessiot theory. It is a Galois Theory of
solvability of linear ordinary differential equations. In
its modern version, this is usually considered (in a
highly algebraic, non-geometric) way as a part of differential algebra (see Kolchin [1]). In fact, Picard and
Vessiot's original ideas were closely related to Lie's.
In a later chapter, I will sketch a development from this
point of view.*

## 2.4  RELATION TO ALGEBRAIC INVARIANT THEORY

To illustrate the preceding general considerations
I shall indicate briefly their relation to the older invariant theory of <u>Cayley</u>, <u>Sylvester</u> and their successors.  In
the binary form

$$a_n x^n + a_{n-1} x^{n-1} y + \cdots + a_1 xy^{n-1} + ay^n = F$$

introduce new variables  $x_1, y_1$  by a linear substitution

$$x = \ell x_1 + m y_1, \qquad y = n x_1 + p y_1 . \qquad (2.4.1)$$

Then  $F$  assumes the analogous form

$$F = b_n x_1^n + b_{n-1} x_1^{n-1} y_1 + \cdots + b_1 x_1 y_1^{n-1} + b y_1^n ,$$

where the new coefficients  $b_k$  are functions of  $\ell, m, n, p$
and the  $a_i$ :

$$b_k = \Pi_k(a, a_1, \ldots, a_n; \ell, m, n, p) . \qquad (2.4.2)$$

These equations (2.4.2) determine a group, and a function of
the  $a_k$  which admits this group is an absolute invariant
of  $F$  with respect to the linear group (2.4.1).

To compute these invariants, I formed therefore the
infinitesimal transformation of the group  : $b_k = \Pi_k$,
which presents no difficulty, and thereby obtained a complete
system, first found by <u>Cayley</u>, whose solutions are the
invariants sought.

Noting that the equations (2.4.1) and (2.4.2), taken together, form a group, one seeks the functions of x,y and the $a_k$ which are invariant with respect to this group, and in this way obtains the covariants of the form F. In this special case my theory coincides with the foundation of the old invariant theory (especially that of binary forms).

*COMMENTS*

*Lie's approach to <u>algebraic</u> invariant theory is developed in greater detail in Lie and Scheffers' book "Continuerliche Grüppen". The relations between Lie group theory and classical algebraic invariant theory are rather mysterious, even today, although in recent years there has been a revival of interest, particularly from the point of view of algebraic geometry.*

Chapter 3

DIFFERENTIAL INVARIANTS OF CONTINUOUS
FINITE GROUPS

The general consideration of differential equations
which admit a continuous group belongs, as far as I know,
to me.

## 3.1    MY WORK ON DIFFERENTIAL INVARIANTS

In almost all of my works of 1871-72 I gave indications of the use of the infinitesimal transformations which
take a given differential equation into itself.  I assumed
that the infinitesimal transformations determine a group,
and my first efforts dealt with the case where not only the
infinitesimal but also the <u>finite</u> transformations of the
group are known.$^{*}$  But I soon realized that considering just
the infinitesimal transformations led to as great a reduction in the order of the integrations involved as I could
obtain in any case, <u>so that in my next works I restricted
myself to the case where only the infinitesimal transformations are known</u>.  But it didn't escape my attention that
when the finite transformations are given, a certain formal
simplification can be attained by an appropriate choice of

---

$^{*}$ To assume that not only the infinitesimal but also the
corresponding finite transformations are known is equivalent
to assuming known the integral curves described by the
infinitesimal transformations.

variables. In 1882 I again took up the hypothesis that the
finite transformations are known, and I showed in detail
what advantage can be gotten from this.

I gave a concise program for all my later work in
this area in the note Zur Theorie der Differentialprobleme
(On the theory of differential problems) (Ges. d. Wiss. zu
Christiania 1872 [Collected Papers Vol. III, paper V, p. 27,
lines 15-5 from the bottom]), to wit:

"I have succeeded in extending my work on partial
differential equations with infinitesimal transformations
in many directions, in particular, to the Pfaffian problem
and to simultaneous systems of ordinary equations. I considered both permutable transformations and those which form
a group. It is possible either to set up at once a certain
number of integrals or to divide the problem into simpler
ones. Simplifications of another kind occur when certain
differential equations, which in some sense correspond to
the transformations, can be integrated.[*] These considerations subsume many old and new theories."

In the Göttinger Nachrichten of Dec. 1874 [Collected
Papers Vol. V, paper I] I gave a remarkable and fundamental

---

[*] In my later terminology this can be formulated more precisely as: "Simplifications of another kind occur when the
equations $B_k f = 0$ corresponding to the known infinitesimal
transformations $B_k$ can be integrated, in other words when
the finite equations of the group are known. It is then
possible to introduce suitable new variables."

reduction of all finite continuous groups of contact-
transformations of a plane to certain canonical forms.  At
the same time I gave a thorough consideration to the invariant differential equations of orders one, two and three
belonging to these groups.  My classification of these groups
was based on considering the invariant differential equations
of lowest order.  I expressed the significance of these
investigations for the general theory of differential equations at the end of the note cited [loc. cit. p. 7, line 7
from the bottom - 8, line 14]:

    "But I should like especially to bring out the rela-
tion of these considerations to the theory of differential
equations.

    "If one has a differential equation of any order for
two variables, it may admit contact-transformations into
itself, which then must form one of the listed groups.
Hence, a classification of these equations can be based on
this, and this yields a rational theory of the integration
of equations which admit transformations into themselves.
An example of such a class is given by the linear equations
together with all equations derived from them by contact-
transformations ...

    "For partial differential equations of any order in
any number of variables there are similar considerations,

and this indicates a fruitful direction of research. Determining the contact-transformations which take a first-order
partial differential equation into itself is equivalent to
integrating it."

On many other occasions also I have emphasized that
my theory of transformation groups provides important new
points of view for the general theory of differential equations.  See, e.g., Archiv for Math. og Naturv. Vol. I,
p. 153 [Collected Papers Vol. V, paper III, p. 42, lines
10-6 from the bottom], where I said:  "Later papers will ...
develop new points of view for the general theory of differential equations in connection with the theories here" (1876).
Soo also p. 19 of this volume;  as well as Math. Ann.
Vol. XVI, p. 441 and pp. 525-528, etc. [Collected Papers,
Vol. V, paper II, p. 9;  Vol. VI, paper I (Vol. XI of "Interdisciplinary Mathematics"), p. 1 and pp. 90-94].

In the Abhandlungen der Gesellschaft der Wissenschaften
zu Christiania for Nov. 1874 [Collected Papers Vol. III,
papers XIII, XIV] (cf. also Math. Ann. Vol. XI, p. 487
[Collected Papers Vol. IV, paper III, Section II]).  I developed in detail the foundations of a general theory of the
integration of a complete system:

$$A_1 f = 0 \ , \ldots, \ A_q f = 0 \qquad (x_1, \ldots, x_n)$$

which admits a number of known infinitesimal transformations.
I cite the following from the beginning and the end of this
work [Collected Papers Vol. III, paper XIV, p. 188, lines
12-17, 20-23, p. 204, line 8f., p. 205, lines 7-5 from the
bottom]:

"I succeeded in developing a rational theory which
in all probability is the largest possible. At a later time
I will take up the question of whether it is possible to get
any greater advantage from the known transformations, to
make them more precise and bring their solution closer, if
not to complete it.... In reality the theory of transformation groups which I have recently developed by way of
suggestion plays a fundamental role; of course, in the
present work this has not been clearly brought out....

"For the moment I must content myself with laying
the foundations and working through some cases.... The
application of these theories to differential equations of
arbitrary order in two variables which admit certain infinitesimal contact-transformations is of particular interest."


3.2    HALPHEN'S WORK ON DIFFERENTIAL INVARIANTS

The classification I announced but did not carry out
in the first-named work is now based on the theorem that

every finite continuous group determines infinitely many differential invariants, which can be defined as the solutions of complete systems, and on the remark that these invariants can be computed if the finite equations of the group are known. In 1884 I had not completed the computations necessary for this classification and had published less.[*]

Meanwhile, <u>Halphen</u> had produced some beautiful, though at first glance special, works[**] bearing the closest relation to my general investigations. He studied the differential invariants of the projective group of the plane (or an n-dimensional manifold) and at the same time considered the integration theory of ordinary differential equations which admit such a group. In this he called attention to the relations of his investigations to <u>Klein</u>'s and to my old works on curves which admit infinitely many linear transformations. On the other hand he seems not to have known my other, more far-reaching works in this area.

---

[*] See my works of 1882 and 1883 on the equations

$$f(x,y,y',\ldots,y^{(m)}) = 0$$

which admit a continuous group. (Archiv for Math. og Naturv. Vol. VII, VIII, 1882, 1883) [Collected Papers Vol. V, papers IX, X, XI, XIV].

[**] Comptes Rendus Vol. 81, p. 1053, 1975; Journal de Math., Nov. 1876; Thèse, Paris 1878; Sur les invariants differentiels des courbes gauches, Journal de l'école polytechnique 1880.

Of course, it would never occur to me to deny the
great service of Halphen's distinguished investigations
in this direction and of his more recent, deep works on
linear differential equations.  But one will allow me to
assert that his older works mentioned here have their
origin, to a not inconsiderable extent, in my general
ideas, which, in my opinion, were first developed by me.


*COMMENTS*

*Lie would no doubt have been very pleased to see
Wilczynski's beautiful book* [1] *on projective differential
geometry (which this subject eventually became), which gave
full credit to his ideas as the conceptual foundation of
the subject!  This theory is one of the simplest and most
interesting examples of Lie's differential invariant
theory.  I will briefly describe it in a later chapter.*

3.3   THE COMPLETE SYSTEM OF EQUATIONS FOR THE DIFFERENTIAL
      INVARIANTS

I consider a completely arbitrary finite continuous
group in the variables  $x, y, z, \ldots, u, v, w, \ldots$ .  If the
transformation equations defining the group

$$x' = F(x, y, z, \ldots, u, v, w, \ldots, a_1, a_2, \ldots, a_r) \quad ,$$

.          .          .          .          .

$$u' = f(x, y, z, \ldots, u, v, w, \ldots, a_1, a_2, \ldots, a_r) \quad , \quad (3.3.1)$$

.          .          .          .          .

contain  $r$  essential parameters, then our group contains
$r$  independent infinitesimal transformations, which I
denote by the common symbol

$$B = X \frac{\partial}{\partial x} + Y \frac{\partial}{\partial y} + Z \frac{\partial}{\partial z} + \cdots + U \frac{\partial}{\partial u} + V \frac{\partial}{\partial v} + W \frac{\partial}{\partial w} + \cdots$$

Now, if  $u, v, w, \ldots$  are given as functions of  $x, y, z, \ldots$,
then  $u', v', w', \ldots$  are functions of  $x', y', z' \ldots$ .  I put

$$\frac{\partial^{m+n+p+\cdots} F}{\partial x^m \partial y^n \partial z^p \ldots} = F_{m,n,p\ldots} \quad ,$$

$$\frac{\partial^{m+n+p+\cdots} F'}{\partial x'^m \partial y'^n \partial z'^p \cdots} = F'_{m,n,p,\ldots} \quad ;$$

then the transformation equations (3.3.1) determine not only $x',y',z',\ldots,u',v',w',\ldots$ but also the derivations of orders $1,2,\ldots,N$:

$$u'_{m,n,p,\ldots}, \quad v'_{m,n,p,\ldots}, \quad w'_{m,n,p,\ldots}$$

as functions of

$$x,y,z,\ldots,u,v,w,\ldots,u_{m,n,p,\ldots}, \quad v_{m,n,p,\ldots}, \quad w_{m,n,p,\ldots},\ldots,$$

where $m,n,p,\ldots$ vary over all possible values for which

$$m+n+p+\cdots \leq N \quad .$$

This dependence is expressed by certain relations

$$u'_{m,n,p,\ldots} = \Phi(x,y,z,\ldots,u,v,w,\ldots,u_{m,n,p,\ldots},\ldots)$$

$$(3.3.2)$$

which, together with (3.3.1), form a group with the $r$ parameters $a_1,\ldots,a_r$.

The expressions for the infinitesimal transformations of this group are found as follows. Under the infinitesimal transformation $B$, the quantities $x,y,z,\ldots$ receive the increments

$$\delta x = X\delta t, \quad \delta y = Y\delta t, \ldots, \quad \delta u = U\delta t, \quad \delta v = V\delta t, \ldots$$

Hence if we put

$$du = \frac{\partial u}{\partial x}\, dx + \frac{\partial u}{\partial y}\, dy + \frac{\partial u}{\partial z}\, dz + \cdots,$$

think of this equation as <u>varying</u>, and introduce the above values of $\delta x, \ldots, \delta w$, we obtain

$$\frac{\delta du}{\delta t} = dU = \frac{\partial u}{\partial x}\, dX + \frac{\partial u}{\partial y}\, dY + \frac{\partial u}{\partial z}\, dZ + \cdots +$$

$$+ \frac{\delta}{\delta t}\frac{\partial u}{\partial x}\cdot dx + \frac{\delta}{\delta t}\frac{\partial u}{\partial y}\cdot dy + \frac{\delta}{\delta t}\frac{\partial u}{\partial z}\cdot dz + \cdots$$

which is equivalent to:

$$\frac{\delta}{\delta t}\frac{\partial u}{\partial x} = \frac{dU}{dx} - \frac{\partial u}{\partial x}\frac{dX}{dx} - \frac{\partial u}{\partial y}\frac{dY}{dx} - \frac{\partial u}{\partial z}\frac{dZ}{dx} \cdots,$$

$$\frac{\delta}{\delta t}\frac{\partial u}{\partial y} = \frac{dU}{dy} - \frac{\partial u}{\partial x}\frac{dX}{dy} - \frac{\partial u}{\partial y}\frac{dY}{dy} - \frac{\partial u}{\partial z}\frac{dZ}{dy} \cdots,$$

$$\frac{\delta}{\delta t}\frac{\partial u}{\partial z} = \frac{dU}{dz} - \frac{\partial u}{\partial x}\frac{dX}{dz} - \frac{\partial u}{\partial y}\frac{dY}{dz} - \frac{\partial u}{\partial z}\frac{dZ}{dz} \cdots,$$

In using these formulas, which are due to <u>Poisson</u>, one must remember that $U, X, Y, Z, \ldots$ depend on $x, y, z, \ldots$, $u, v, w, \ldots$, and that $u, v, w, \ldots$ are to be considered functions of $x, y, z, \ldots$ .

In a similar way one computes successively the increments of all the quantities

$$u_{m,n,p,\ldots},\ v_{m,n,p,\ldots},\ w_{m,n,p,\ldots}\ ,$$

under the infinitesimal transformation B. Denoting these increments by

$$U_{(m,n,p,\ldots)}\delta t,\ V_{(m,n,p,\ldots)}\delta t,\ W_{(m,n,p,\ldots)}\delta t,\ldots\ ,$$

one has

$$\tilde{B} = X\frac{\partial}{\partial x} + Y\frac{\partial}{\partial y} + Z\frac{\partial}{\partial z} + \cdots + U\frac{\partial}{\partial u} + V\frac{\partial}{\partial v} + W\frac{\partial}{\partial w} + \cdots +$$

$$+ \sum U_{(m,n,p,\ldots)}\frac{\partial}{\partial U_{m,n,p,\ldots}} + \sum V_{(m,n,p,\ldots)}\frac{\partial}{\partial V_{(m,n,p,\ldots)}}$$

$$+ \sum W_{(m,n,p,\ldots)}\frac{\partial}{\partial W_{(m,n,p,\ldots)}} + \cdots$$

$$(m+n+p+\cdots \leq N)\ .$$

This is the expression sought for the infinitesimal transformation $\tilde{B}$ of the group (3.3.1), (3.3.2).

If N is so large that the expressions $\tilde{B}f$ contain more than r derivations of f, applying what was said in §2.2 to the group $\tilde{B}$,[*] gives at once the theorem:

[*] Note that if r infinitesimal transformations
$$B_k = X_k\frac{\partial}{\partial x} + Y_k\frac{\partial}{\partial y} + \cdots + W_k\frac{\partial}{\partial w} + \cdots$$
satisfy relations $[B_i,B_k] = \sum c_{iks}B_s$, then it can be shown directly that
$$\tilde{B}_1,\ldots,\tilde{B}_r$$
satisfy the same relations.

<u>Theorem 3.3.1</u>. Every finite continuous group of transforma-
tions has infinitely many differential invariants, which
can be defined as the solutions of complete systems.  If
one knows the finite equation of the group, one can find
the expressions for an arbitrary number of differential
invariants by permissible operations.  The invariant systems
of differential equations of our group (3.3.1), (3.3.2) are
found by the rules given above.

In earlier works (Archiv for Math. og Naturv, Vol.
VIII, p. 187, 249, 37] [Collected Papers Vol. V,  papers X,
XI, XIV]) I dealt exhaustively with the case that the infini-
tesimal transformations of our group are of the form

$$X(x,u) \frac{\partial}{\partial x} + U(x,u) \frac{\partial}{\partial u} \quad ,$$

where  u  is a function of  x.

In the last of these three papers I dealt in detail
with the differential invariants of a group whose infinitesimal transformations

$$U(u,v) \frac{\partial}{\partial u} + V(u,v) \frac{\partial}{\partial v}$$

contain only the dependent variables  u,v,  not the independent variables  x,y,  These invariants are functions of

$$u,v, \ \frac{\partial u}{\partial x}, \ \frac{\partial u}{\partial y}, \ \frac{\partial v}{\partial x}, \ \frac{\partial v}{\partial y}, \cdots$$

If one differentiates such an invariant with respect, to  x
or  y,  one obtains a new invariant, as is easily seen.

  Likewise, in the general case, if enough differential
invariants have been computed, it is possible to derive new
invariants from them (more precisely, by forming the quo-
tients of the two Jacobians).  The finite transformations
of the group need not be known for this, but I will not go
into this further now.


3.4    *COMMENTS ON CHAPTER 3*

  *The formalism described in Chapter A is ideally*
*suited to description of these ideas in their modern form.*

  *Let   X   and   Z   be manifolds,   X   is called the*
*independent variable manifold,   Z   is called the dependent*
*variable manifold.   For each positive integer   r,*

$$M^r(X,Z)$$

*denotes the  r-th order mapping elements.   If*

$$n = \dim X \quad,$$

*it is an open subset of the contact element manifold*

$$C^r(X \times Z, n) \quad.$$

  *Let   G   be a Lie transformation group acting on*
*X × Z.   (See my Comments in LG, Vol. 1  for details about*

*what is meant here.)  The* <u>*prolongation of*</u> *G,  as defined
in Chapter A, is a Lie transformation group on*  $C^r(X \times Z, n)$.
*Since*  $M^r(X,Z)$  *is an open subset of*  $C^r(X \times Z, n)$,  *G  acts
as a* <u>*local Lie group*</u> *on*  $M^r(X,Z)$.  *This is the action that
Lie deals with.*

<u>*Remark*</u>.  *More generally, one can begin with*  G  *on a* <u>*local
Lie transformation group*</u> *on*  X × Z.  *It prolongs to a local
action of*  G  *on*  $M^r(X,Z)$.

<u>*Definition*</u>.  *A function*

$$\Omega: M^r(X,Z) \to R$$

*is a* <u>*differential invariant for the action of*</u>  G  *if*

$$\Omega(g^r(\gamma)) \;=\; \Omega(g\gamma) \qquad\qquad (4.1)$$

$$\text{\textit{for all}}\ \ \gamma \in M^r(X,Z),\ \ \text{\textit{all}}\ \ g \in G.$$

*(Recall that*  $g^r$  *denotes the* <u>*prolongation*</u> *of the action
of*  g,  *as described in Chapter A.)*

        *The* <u>*Cayley-Clebsch*</u> *(complete)* <u>*differential equation
system*</u> *can be described as follows.  Let*  G̰  *denote the
Lie algebra of*  G.  *Since*  G  *is given as a Lie transformation group on*  X × Z,  G̰  *is given as a Lie subalgebra of*

$$V(X \times Z)\ \ .$$

*The prolongation operator*

$$A \to A^r$$

*defines* $\underset{\sim}{G}$ *as a Lie algebra of vector fields on* $M^r(X,Z)$.
*If* G *is a* <u>*connected Lie group*</u>, *a function* $\Omega: M^r(X,Z) \to R$
*is invariant under the prolongation of* G, *i.e., is a*
<u>*differential invariant of the action of*</u> G <u>*on*</u> X × Z *if*
*and only if*

$$A^r(\Omega) \;=\; 0 \qquad\qquad\qquad (4.2)$$

*for all* A ε $\underset{\sim}{G}$ .

*Since* $\underset{\sim}{G}$ *forms a Lie algebra, 4.2 is what is known classi-*
*cally as a* <u>*complete*</u> *(or* <u>*completely integrable*</u>*)* <u>*system*</u> *(Of*
*course, the vector field system generated by* $\underset{\sim}{G}$ *on* $M^r(X,Z)$
*will have* <u>*singularities*</u>. *The classical authors ignored*
*this fact, which makes their results not completely rigorous,*
*at least by modern standards.)*

*The concept of a "differential equation is invariant*
*under* G" *is defined in a similar way. As described in*
*Chapter A, a* <u>*differential equation system*</u>, *with* X *as* <u>*indep-*</u>
<u>*endent variable*</u>, Z *as* <u>*dependent variable*</u>, *is defined as a*
*differentiable subset*

$$DE \subset M^r(X,Z) \quad .$$

G *leaves the* <u>*differential equation system invariant*</u> *if*

$$g^r(DE) \subset DE \qquad\qquad\qquad (4.3)$$

*for all* g ε G .

*Here is one way of constructing such invariant equations. Let us say that a function*

$$\Omega: M^r(X,Z) \to R$$

*is a <u>relative differential invariant</u> if the following condition is satisfied:*

> *There is a function   f ε F(M$^r$(X,Z))*
>
> *such that*
>
> $$(g^r)^*(\Omega) = f\Omega \quad .$$   *(4.4)*
>
> *for all  g ε G  .*

*Set:*

> DE = *set of points of*  $M^r(X,Z)$
> *on which*   $\Omega = 0$ .                   *(4.5)*

*It follows from 4.4 that*

$$g^r(DE) \subset DE \quad .$$

*Hence:*

> *A <u>relative</u> r-th <u>order differential</u>*
> *<u>invariant of</u>  G  <u>determines an</u>*
> *<u>invariant</u> r-th <u>order differential</u>*
> *<u>equation</u>.*

*Of course, Lie is much too casual by modern standards in his statement of Theorem 3.3.1. (Here, he is playing the role of the Euler of differential geometry that I discuss in the Preface.) For example, to apply (even locally) the Jacobi-Clebsch integrability theorem (which is more-or-less equivalent to what we now call the Frobenius Complete Integrability Theorem) one must know that the rank of the equations is constant. Since Lie does say he is considering a <u>finite</u> continuous group, i.e., a finite dimensional Lie algebra of vector fields, we do know that there is at least an open subset of the mapping element space where this rank is constant, (i.e., the union of the <u>orbits of maximal dimension</u>). What happens in the way of existence of invariants at the <u>singular orbits</u> is just not known.*

Chapter 4

DIFFERENTIAL INVARIANTS OF
INFINITE CONTINUOUS GROUPS

## 4.1    INFINITE CONTINUOUS GROUPS

I say that a continuous family of transformations
forms an infinite continuous group if

1)   the composition of two transformations of the
family is again one,

2)   every finite transformation of the family is
generated by infinite iteration of an infinitesimal transformation of the family,

3)   the family contains infinitely many linearly
independent infinitesimal transformations.

We restrict ourselves to the case where, if

$$B = \xi_1 \frac{\partial}{\partial x_1} + \cdots + \xi_n \frac{\partial}{\partial x_n}$$

is the general symbol of an infinitesimal transformation of
a group, the $\xi_i$ are determined as functions of $x_1, \ldots, x_n$
by certain partial differential equations

$$\Omega_i \left( x_1, \ldots, x_n, \xi_1, \ldots, \xi_n, \frac{\partial \xi_1}{\partial x_1}, \ldots \right) = 0$$

These equations must be linear, since the infinitesimal
transformations of the group form a vector space.   I call
these linear partial differential equations

69

$$0 = \sum_i f_i \xi_i + \sum g_{ik} \frac{\partial \xi_i}{\partial x_k} + \sum h_{ikj} \frac{\partial^2 \xi_i}{\partial x_k \partial x_j} + \cdots$$

the <u>defining equations of the group</u>.

The simplest example of an infinite group is the totality of all point- or contact-transformations of an n-dimensional space. In the case of the group of all point-transformations of the manifold $x_1, \ldots, x_n$, the defining equations $Bf = \sum \xi_k f_{x_k}$ for the infinitesimal transformations of the group reduce to the identity $0 = 0$.

A second example is the group of all contact-transformations which take a given first-order partial differential equation into itself.[*]

---

[*] If $u_1, u_2, \ldots, u_r$ are functions of $x_1, \ldots, x_n, p_1, \ldots, p_n$ with relations of the form $(u_i, u_k) = f_{ik}(u_1, \ldots, u_r)$, and if $\Omega$ is an arbitrary function of the $u_k$, then the set of all infinitesimal transformations whose (common) symbol is $Bf = (\Omega, f)$ is an infinite group. ($(u_i, u_k)$ denotes the Poisson bracket.) For this reason I have long called the set of the $u_k$'s a <u>group</u>. (Ges. d. Wiss. zu Christiania 1872, p. 134; 1873, p. 18 and 59; Math. Ann. Vol. VIII, p. 248 and 286 [Collected Papers Vol. III, paper VI, p. 29; VII, p. 34; VIII, p. 71; Vol. IV, paper I, §9, No. 21; §21, No. 44]).

I claim that the linear partial differential equations $(u_1, v) = 0, \ldots, (u_r, v) = 0$ form a complete (or <u>completely integrable</u>) system, whose solutions $v_1, v_2, \ldots, v_{2n-r}$ form a new group (the <u>polar group</u>). Considering the $(u_k, f)$ as symbols of infinitesimal transformations, the $v_i$ are their <u>invariants</u>. But one can also consider both the $u_k$ and the $v_i$ as symbols of infinitesimal transformations; then every transformation of one group commutes with every transformation of the other. In my old synthetic investigations of such groups, I frequently used both these conceptions.

The following theorem is evident but important:
<u>Theorem</u>. If a group $u_1, \ldots, u_r$ is such that each of the equations $u_k = $ const. is integrable, then the $v_k$ can always be specified.

A third example is the group of all point-transformations which take a given linear partial differential equation of arbitrary order into itself.

A fourth example is the group of all point-transformations which take a <u>nonlinear</u> second-order equation $s = e^{kz}$
into itself.

I have considered the above (and other) examples of
infinite groups for a long time and thoroughly.

In 1872 I gave some brief indications of the existence of invariants of a partial differential equation of
arbitrary order with respect to all contact- or point-
transformations (Gött. Nachr. 1872, No. 25, pp. 478-479;
Ges. d. Wiss. zu Christiania 1872, Zur Theorie der Diffpr.,
p. 132) [Collected Papers Vol. III, paper IV, p. 19ff;
paper V, p. 27]. But it was a long time before I succeeded
in laying the foundations of a general theory of infinite
continuous groups (see in particular:  Abhandlungen der
Ges. d. Wiss. zu Christiania 1883, No. 12 [Collected Papers
Vol. V, paper XIII]).  Referring to these and my older works
for the rest, I restrict myself here to the following remarks,
which suffice for what follows.

Let there be given an arbitrary finite or infinite
transformation group of the manifold $x_1,...,x_n$.  If

$$B = \xi_1 \frac{\partial}{\partial x_1} + \xi_2 \frac{\partial}{\partial x_2} + \cdots + \xi_n \frac{\partial}{\partial x_n} \quad ,$$

$$C = \eta_1 \frac{\partial}{\partial x_1} + \eta_2 \frac{\partial}{\partial x_2} + \cdots + \eta_n \frac{\partial}{\partial x_n}$$

are two infinitesimal transformations of the group, then it is possible to construct new infinitesimal transformations of the group in various ways.

Under the infinitesimal transformation  B,  the x-system goes into the neighboring system

$$x_i + Bx_i \delta t = x_i + \xi_i \cdot \delta t \quad .$$

Applying  C  takes this to

$$x_i + \xi_i \cdot \delta t + C(x_i + \xi_i \cdot \delta t) \ \delta \tau$$

Thus, ignoring second-order infinitesimals,  $C \circ B$  takes the x-system to

$$x_i + \xi_i \cdot \delta t + \eta_i \cdot \delta \tau$$

Thus our group contains every infinitesimal transformation under which the  $x_i$  receive the increments

$$\delta x_i = \xi_i \cdot \delta t + \eta_i \cdot \delta \tau$$

This theorem, which we have already mentioned as being obvious, is formulated as:

Theorem 4.1.1.  If  B  and  C  are infinitesimal transformations of a continuous group, so is  $c_1 B + c_2 C$, with the arbitrary constant  $c_1 : c_2$.

We can construct new infinitesimal transformations
in a different way.  Applying  B  takes the $x_i$-system to
the new position

$$x_i' \;=\; x_i + \delta t \cdot \xi_i + \frac{1}{2}\,\delta t^2 \cdot B\xi_i \quad,$$

in which we disregarded third-order infinitesimals.  Applying  C  now takes the $x_i'$-system to the position

$$x_i'' \;=\; x_i + \delta t \cdot \xi_i + \frac{1}{2}\,\delta t^2 \cdot B\xi_i + \delta\tau \cdot \eta_i + \delta t \cdot \delta\tau \cdot C\xi_i$$
$$+ \frac{1}{2}\,\delta\tau^2 \cdot C\eta_i \quad.$$

On the other hand applying  C  first to the $x_i$-system
brings it to the position

$$(x_i') \;=\; x_i + \delta\tau \cdot \eta_i + \frac{1}{2}\,\delta\tau^2 \cdot C\eta_i \quad,$$

and this is taken by  B  to the position

$$(x_i)'' \;=\; x_i + \delta\tau \cdot \eta_i + \frac{1}{2}\,\delta\tau^2 \cdot C\eta_i + \delta t \cdot \xi_i + \delta t \cdot \delta\tau \cdot B\eta_i$$
$$+ \frac{1}{2}\,\delta t^2 \cdot B\xi_i \quad.$$

It is now clear that the infinitesimal transformation taking
the $x_i''$-system to the  $(x_i)''$-system belongs to our group.
But since

$$(x_i)'' - x_i'' \;=\; \delta t \cdot \delta\tau\,(B\eta_i - C\xi_i) \quad,$$

we get the following fundamental theorem, which I discovered in 1872:

<u>Theorem 4.1.2</u>.  If a continuous group contains the two
infinitesimal transformations

$$B = \sum \xi_k \frac{\partial}{\partial x_k} \qquad \text{and} \qquad C = \sum \eta_k \frac{\partial}{\partial x_k} \quad ,$$

then it also contains the infinitesimal transformation

$$\sum_i (B\eta_i - C\xi_i) \frac{\partial}{\partial x_i} \quad ,$$

whose symbol, as is well-known, can be brought to the two
equivalent forms

$$B \circ C - C \circ B = [B,C] \quad .^{*}$$

If all transformations of the one-parameter groups generated by  B  and  C  commute with one another, then  $[B,C] = 0$.
The converse also holds, since if  $[B,C] = 0$,  then by introducing new variables  $y_k$,  one can bring  B  and  C  into
the form

$$B = \frac{\partial}{\partial y_1} , \qquad C = \frac{\partial}{\partial y_2}$$

or

$$B = \frac{\partial}{\partial y_1} , \qquad C = y_2 \frac{\partial}{\partial y_1} \quad .$$

---

$^{*}$  From the theorem of the text follows, as I noted long ago,
the following important corollary, among other things:  If
a system of differential equations admits the two transformations  B  and  C,  then it also admits  $[B,C]$.  In the
case where the system of equations consists of a single
<u>first-order</u> partial differential equations, this is the
so-called <u>Poisson-Jacobi</u> theorem.

(See e.g., Ges. d. Wiss. zu Christiania 1872;  my Archiv
Vol. III, pp. 100-105;  Vol. VII, p. 180 [Collected Papers
Vol. III, paper I, p. 2, 595;  Vol. V, paper IV, pp. 83-87;
paper VII, p. 225]).  We have then my old theorem:

Theorem 4.1.3.  If  $[B,C] = 0$,  then the two infinitesimal
transformations commute.

The method that has given us Theorem 4.1.1 and
Theorem 4.1.2 can be generalized, as one sees without
difficulty.  This gives new methods of constructing arbitrary many infinitesimal transformations of any group
containing  B  and  C.  But it can be shown (Archiv for
Math. og Naturv. Vol. III, p. 100 [Collected Papers Vol. V,
paper IV, p. 84]), that all the methods one finds in this
way amount only to iterated applications of Theorem 4.1.2.
It is obvious from that theorem that  $[[B,C],B]$  and
$[[B,C],C]$  are the symbols of infinitesimal transformations
of our group.[*]

---
[*]  The following remarks are in order, although they will not
be used in this paper.  Let there be given a continuous
family of infinitesimal transformations  B,  of which we
choose two, say  $B_1$  and  $B_2$,  arbitrarily.  Then if  $[B_1,B_2]$
and all the infinitesimal transformations  $c_1B_1 + c_2B_2$  belong
to our family, then it is natural to conjecture that there
is a continuous group whose infinitesimal transformations
form the given family.

If the family contains only a finite number of independent transformations, this conjecture can be verified
without great difficulty (See Archiv for Math. og Naturv.

*COMMENTS ON SECTION 4.1*

*Lie certainly covers a wealth of ideas in this section! In fact, much of this material has never been developed rigorously, or is just now in the process of development. (See Kumpera-Spencer [1]). I will now describe it as best as I can in this limited space.*

*A basic question in understanding Lie's work is: What does he mean by a <u>continuous group</u>? The modern mathematician might be tempted to interpret this in terms of what we now call <u>the theory of topological groups</u>. (See Pontrjagin [1]). Say, that it might be a connected topological group which acts (continuously) as groups of diffeomorphisms of a manifold X. In fact, this is not really satisfactory, since Lie definitely had in mind that the individual transformations making up the group should be <u>generated by infinitesimal transformations</u>. One might then think that the relevant object is an <u>infinite dimensional manifold version</u> of what we now call a "Lie group", i.e., a finite dimensional manifold with a differentiable group-law. While there is a satisfactory theory of this sort*

---

Vol. III, p. 100 [Collected Papers Vol. V, paper IV, p. 84, Theorem I]).

On the other hand if our family contains infinitely many independent infinitesimal transformations, the resolution of this question is not so simple. I believe that I have proved it in general, and in any case it is true for infinitesimal <u>point</u>- or <u>contact</u>-transformations of a <u>plane</u>.

*available for certain groups of this type (e.g., the group
of volume preserving diffeomorphisms of a manifold--see
Ebin and Marsden [1], Imori [1]), it is not yet developed
to the extent that would be required to cover the main
elements of Lie's work.*

*In fact, in the state of our present knowledge, it
is probably not possible to give a general, but useful,
definition.  I suggest that the reader think of a "continuous group" as being <u>something</u> like the following object:*

> *A triple consisting of an ordinary (finite
> dimensional) manifold* X, *a group* G *of
> diffeomorphisms on* X *and a Lie algebra*
> G̰ *of vector fields on* X *such that:*
>
> *a)  For each* A ε G̰, *the one-parameter
>      group of diffeomorphisms of* X *gener-
>      ated by* A *lies in* G
>
> *b)  Every* g ε G *can be written as the
>      product of elements of* G *which lie
>      on one-parameter subgroups generated
>      by elements of* G̰

*There are two directions in which these ideas might
be modified.  First, one should allow for the possibility
of "localization", and perhaps also for the operations
defined by "formal power series" or some other "generalized*

*function" procedure.   Second, we should allow the possibility*
*that <u>all elements of</u>  G  <u>do not have inverses which lie in</u>*
*G,  i.e.,  G <u>forms a semigroup</u>.  Similarly, the infinitesi-*
*mal generator  G̰  may not form a vector space, but may have*
*more general structure, e.g., a "cone".  Lie obviously had*
*both of these possibilities in mind.*

*Now, Lie also recognized that it was difficult to*
*say very much at this level of generality.  His motivation*
*was always to <u>develop the connections between group theory</u>*
*<u>and the theory of differential equations</u>.  Accordingly, he*
*chose as a realistic alternative the less general assumption*
*that "the transformations of the group are solutions of a*
*given system of differential equations".  I have described*
*such objects in Volume IX, and will not repeat the discus-*
*sion here.  This definition in terms of differential equa-*
*tions was later used by E. Cartan in his work on "infinite*
*dimensional groups", and has also formed the basis for the*
*modern work, e.g., see Kumpera and Spencer [1].*

*In any case, the way to study and understand Lie is*
*not to expect even an approximation to modern standards of*
*precision in terms of general definitions and concepts, but*
*to look at his examples and his methods for dealing with*
*these examples.  (In this respect, Lie is closer in spirit*
*to the 18-th century mathematicians, especially Euler, than*
*to his contemporaries and peers like Weierstrass, Kronecker,*

*Poincaré, etc.) In this section Lie briefly mentions a few examples--we shall encounter them, and many others, as we proceed into Lie's work.*

## 4.2   EXAMPLES

In turning now to proving the general existence of differential invariants of an arbitrary infinite group, we begin with a discussion of two simple examples in order to ease as much as possible the understanding of the general theory.

We consider all infinitesimal transformations of the form

$$B = X(x) \frac{\partial}{\partial x} + yX' \frac{\partial}{\partial y} + zX' \frac{\partial}{\partial z} ,$$

where X is an arbitrary function of x, and X' is its derivative. We choose two of these transformations

$$B_i = X_i \frac{\partial}{\partial x} + yX_i' \frac{\partial}{\partial y} + zX_i' \frac{\partial}{\partial z} , \qquad (i = 1,2);$$

then

$$[B_1,B_2] = (X_1X_2'-X_2X_1') \frac{\partial}{\partial x} + y(X_1X_2''-X_2X_1'') \frac{\partial}{\partial y}$$

$$+ z(X_1X_2''-X_2X_1'') \frac{\partial}{\partial z}$$

assumes the form

$$[B_1, B_2] \;=\; \xi \frac{\partial}{\partial x} + y\xi' \frac{\partial}{\partial y} + z\xi' \frac{\partial}{\partial z}$$

when one makes the substitution

$$X_1 X_2' - X_2 X_1' \;=\; \xi(x) \quad .$$

Hence it is natural to conjecture that there is an infinite
group whose infinitesimal transformations are just the
family of the B's.

To show this in the simplest way one verifies first
that the transformation equations

$$x_1 \;=\; F(x), \qquad y_1 \;=\; yF'(x), \qquad z_1 \;=\; zF'(x)$$

form an infinite group for any function F. Putting

$$F(x) \;=\; x + X(x)\delta t \quad ,$$

one sees that this group contains all infinitesimal transformations of the form

$$x_1 \;=\; x + X\delta t, \qquad y_1 \;=\; y + yX'\delta t, \qquad z_1 \;=\; z + zX'\delta t,$$

i.e., all the infinitesimal transformations B and no others.

It is easy to see that this infinite group determines
not only differential invariants but also invariant functions
of $x,y,z$ alone. For if in the equation

$$X \frac{\partial}{\partial x} + y \cdot X' \frac{\partial f}{\partial y} + z \cdot X' \frac{\partial f}{\partial z} \;=\; 0$$

one lets X vary over arbitrary many functions of $x$, the
totality of equations one gets in this way is equivalent to
the two:

$$\frac{\partial f}{\partial x} = 0, \qquad y\frac{\partial f}{\partial y} + z\frac{\partial f}{\partial z} = 0$$

These form a complete system with the solution $y/z$, so that this is an invariant of our infinite group, as can be verified directly.

We can form differential invariants in various ways. For we can adjoin to $x,y,z$ arbitrary many additional quantities $\alpha,\beta,\gamma,\ldots$, which are invariant under the group. We have then a free choice of which of these variables to regard as independent and which as dependent.

First let $x,y,z$ be functions of a single quantity $\alpha$ invariant under the group. Then we obtain the transformation equations

$$\alpha_1 = \alpha, \qquad x_1 = F(x), \qquad y_1 = yF'(x), \qquad z_1 = zF'(x)$$

$$(4.2.1)$$

If we now put

$$\frac{dx}{d\alpha} = x', \ \frac{dy}{d\alpha} = y', \ \frac{dz}{d\alpha} = z', \ \frac{dx_1}{d\alpha} = x_1',\ldots,$$

then the dependence relations among the first derivatives are

$$\left.\begin{array}{l} x_1' = F'(x)x'; \quad y_1' = y'F'(x) + yF''(x)x'; \\[2mm] \qquad z_1' = z'F'(x) + zF''(x)x' . \end{array}\right\} (4.2.2)$$

It can be verified that the equations (4.2.1) and (4.2.2)
determine an infinite group.  By making the substitution

$$F(x) = x + X(x)\delta t \quad ,$$

one sees that its infinitesimal transformations are of the
form:

$$\delta x = X\delta t, \qquad\qquad \delta y = yX'\delta t, \qquad \delta z = zX'\delta t,$$

$$\delta x' = X'x'\delta t, \qquad\qquad \delta y' = (y'X'+yX''x')\delta t,$$

$$\delta z' = (z'X'+zX''x')\delta t,$$

and hence can be denoted by the symbol

$$B' = X \frac{\partial}{\partial x} + yX' \frac{\partial}{\partial y} + zX' \frac{\partial}{\partial z} + X'x' \frac{\partial}{\partial x} + (y'X'+yx'X'') \frac{\partial}{\partial y'}$$

$$+ (z'X'+zx'X'') \frac{\partial}{\partial z'} \quad .$$

If $X_1, X_2$ are particular values of $X$ and $B'_1, B'_2$ are the
corresponding infinitesimal transformations, then it is
a priori certain (and can be easily verified) that $[B'_1, B'_2]$
is also of the form $B'$.

It now follows that the set of all equations $B'f = 0$
which is equivalent to the system

$$\frac{\partial f}{\partial x} = 0 \quad ,$$

$$y \frac{\partial f}{\partial y} + z \frac{\partial f}{\partial z} + x' \frac{\partial f}{\partial x'} + y' \frac{\partial f}{\partial y'} + z' \frac{\partial f}{\partial z'} = 0 \quad ,$$

$$y \frac{\partial f}{\partial y'} + z \frac{\partial f}{\partial z'} = 0 \quad,$$

is a complete system. The solutions of this complete system

$$\frac{z}{y} \;, \quad \frac{x'}{y} \quad \text{and} \quad \frac{yz'-zy'}{yz} = \frac{d}{d\alpha}\left(\frac{z}{y}\right) \tag{4.2.3}$$

are invariants of the group (4.2.1), (4.2.2) and are differential invariants of the group (4.2.1).

Forming the second derivatives gives

$$x_1'' = F'x'' + F''x'^2 \quad,$$

$$y_1'' = y''F' + 2y'F''x' + yF'''x'^2 + yF''x'' \quad,$$

$$z_1'' = z''F' + 2z'F''x' + zF'''x'^2 + zF''x'' \quad.$$

Taken together with (4.2.1) and (4.2.2) these form an infinite group of transformations of

$$x, y, z, x', y', z', x'', y'', z'' \quad.$$

Setting $F(x) = x + X(x)\delta t,$ one finds that the general expression for the infinitesimal transformation $B''$ of this group is of the form

$$B'' = XA + X'A' + X''A'' + X'''A''' \quad.$$

Here $A, A', A'', A'''$ are determining operators, which are completely independent of the form of the arbitrary function $X$. Therefore all the equations of the form $B''f = 0,$ which are equivalent to the systems of equations

$$Af = 0, \quad A'f = 0, \quad A''f = 0, \quad A'''f = 0,$$

form a complete system with <u>five</u> solutions.

Among these solutions there are three (see (4.2.3)) of order zero or one; the two remaining are the second-order invariants sought. It is clear that one can find infinitely many differential invariants in this way.

There are several other sequences of differential invariants belonging to the infinite group

$$x_1 = F(x), \qquad y_1 = yF', \qquad z_1 = zF' \qquad (4.2.1)$$

with the infinitesimal transformation

$$B = X \frac{\partial}{\partial x} + yX' \frac{\partial}{\partial y} + zX' \frac{\partial}{\partial z} \quad .$$

For example, we can consider $y$ and $z$ as functions of $x$ and put

$$\frac{dy}{dx} = y', \qquad \frac{dz}{dx} = z', \quad \text{etc.}$$

Then

$$y_1' = y' + y \frac{F''}{F'} , \qquad z_1' = z' + z \frac{F''}{F'} ,$$

and these equations, when taken together with (4.2.1), form a group whose general infinitesimal transformation is

$$B' = X \frac{\partial}{\partial x} + yX' \frac{\partial}{\partial y} + zX' \frac{\partial}{\partial z} + yX'' \frac{\partial}{\partial y'} + zX'' \frac{\partial}{\partial z'}$$

The totality of the equations $B'f = 0$ forms the complete system

$$\frac{\partial f}{\partial x} = 0, \qquad y\,\frac{\partial f}{\partial y} + z\,\frac{\partial f}{\partial z} = 0, \qquad y\,\frac{\partial f}{\partial y'} + z\,\frac{\partial f}{\partial z'} = 0$$

with the relations

$$\frac{y}{z}\,, \qquad\qquad \frac{zy'-yz'}{y}\,,$$

which are first-order differential invariants. In the same way one can find invariants of higher order.

To find a third sequence of invariants of our group introduce a quantity $\alpha$ which is invariant under the group and consider it as a function of $x,y,z$. One then obtains two essential first-order differential invariants, and so on.

Note that some invariants may belong to several sequences. For example, our first sequence contains <u>all</u> the invariants of the second.

*COMMENTS ON SECTION 4.2*

*Here is a more intrinsic description of the group described in this section. Let* X *be a manifold. Set:*

G = *group of diffeomorphisms of* X.

*Each* g ε G *acts via* <u>*prolongation*</u> *on the* <u>*tangent vector bundle*</u> T(X):

$$g(v) = g_*(v)$$

*for* v ε T(X).

*Set:*

$$Y = \textit{direct sum vector bundle of}$$

$$T(X) \oplus T(X) \quad .$$

$G$   *acts as direct sum.*

*Thus, a point of*   $Y$   *is a triple:*

$$(x, v_1, v_2) \quad ,$$

$$\textit{with} \quad x \in X; \quad v_1, v_2 \in X_x$$

$g \in G$   *acts as follows:*

$$g(x, v_1, v_2) \;=\; (g(x), g_*(v_1), g_*(v_2)) \quad .$$

*To reduce to Lie's example, suppose:*

$$X = R, \quad \textit{with coordinate} \quad x .$$

*Suppose:*

$$g(x) \;=\; F(x) \quad .$$

*Let*   y   *be the function* :   $T(X) \to R$   *defined as follows:*

$$y(v) \;=\; dx(v) \quad ,$$

$$\textit{for} \quad v \in T(X) \quad .$$

*Thus, the point of*   $T(X)$   *with coordinates*

$$(x, y)$$

*is the point*

$$\left( x, t\, \frac{\partial}{\partial x} \right) \quad \textit{of} \quad T(X)$$

*Hence,*

$$g(x,y) \quad is \ the \ point:$$

$$\left( F(x), yg_*\left(\frac{\partial}{\partial x}\right) \right)$$

*But,* $g^*(x) = F(x)$. *Hence,*

$$g_*\left(\frac{\partial}{\partial x}\right) (x) = \frac{\partial}{\partial x} (F(x)) = F'(x)$$

*Then,*

$$g(x,y) = (F(x), yF'(x))$$

*We see that* Y *is the space of coordinates*

$$(x,y,z) \quad ,$$

*with* G *acting on* Y *by the formulas given by Lie:*

$$g(x,y,z) = (x, F'(x)y, F'(x)z) \quad .$$

To define "differential invariants", two procedures
are sketched by Lie. First, pick Z as any other manifold,
consider

$$M^r(Z,Y) \quad ,$$

and let G act on this space in the natural way. Invariant
functions on this space are called "differential invariants
of the first sequence". Second, consider

$$Y \quad as \ a \ fiber \ space \ over \quad X,$$

with the projection map

$$\pi: Y \to X$$

*defined as follows:*

$$\pi(x, v_1, v_2) = x \quad .$$

*G   acts on   Y   in a <u>fiber preserving way</u>.   Let*

$$\Gamma(Y)$$

*be the space of cross-section maps*

$$\gamma: X \to Y \quad .$$

*G   acts on   $\Gamma(Y)$   in the following way:*

$$g(\gamma)(x) = g(\gamma(g^{-1}x)) \quad .$$

*Now, construct the <u>jet bundles</u>*

$$J^r(Y) \; , \qquad r = 1, 2, \ldots$$

*(See VB.)   They are subspaces of   $M^r(X, Y)$,   consisting of mapping elements which represent <u>cross-section</u> maps.   Let G   act on   $J^r(Y)$   in the natural way--invariant functions are now called "<u>differential invariants of the second sequence</u>".*

*These groups and their associated "differential invariants" are of the greatest importance for physics. (They--and their generalizations--are often called <u>gauge transformations</u>.)   For example, if*

$$X = R^4 \; ,$$

*the space-time manifold of Special Relativity, then cross-sections of the vector bundle*

$$T(X) \rightarrow X$$

*are called <u>vector fields</u> or <u>spin-one</u> systems in physics.*
*(Of course, they are also "vector fields" in the sense of*
*differential geometry.)*

    *Elements of*

$$\Gamma(Y) \quad,$$

*i.e., cross-sections of the fiber space*

$$Y \quad \equiv \quad T(X) \oplus T(X) \rightarrow X$$

*are then identified with pairs of spin-one "particles".*
*(Say a "photon" and a "meson".) Differential invariants of*
*the second type then can obviously serve to construct*
*<u>differential equations</u> for such fields, which are fully*
*<u>invariant</u> under the group G. Of course, Einstein thought*
*of invariance under the group G ($\equiv$ all diffeomorphisms*
*of X) as <u>general covariance</u>.*

    *In fact, Einstein's conception of the gravitational*
*field is very similar to this example. Y is replaced by*
*another fiber space Y' over X, whose fibers are the*
*space of twice-covariant, symetric <u>tensors</u> on X ($\equiv$ a four*
*dimensional manifold). The "differential invariants" of*
*the action of G on $\Gamma(Y')$ (or rather the "relative*
*invariants") serve to define "covariant gravitational*
*fields". For example, the Einstein gravitational equations*
*themselves are of this type.*

## 4.3    THE GROUP OF VOLUME-PRESERVING TRANSFORMATIONS OF THE PLANE

The infinitesimal transformations

$$B = X(x,y) \frac{\partial}{\partial x} + Y(x,y) \frac{\partial}{\partial y}$$

satisfying

$$\frac{\partial X}{\partial x} + \frac{\partial Y}{\partial y} = 0$$

generate an infinite group.  Its transformations are characterized by the fact that they leave invariant all the
"surface spaces" of the Cartesian  x,y-plane.[*]  To find the
differential invariants of this infinite group, introduce
two new quantities  $\bar{x}, \bar{y}$  which are not transformed by the
group, consider  x,y  as functions of  $\bar{x}, \bar{y}$,  and put

$$\frac{\partial x}{\partial \bar{x}} = x_1, \; \frac{\partial x}{\partial \bar{y}} = x_2, \; \frac{\partial y}{\partial \bar{x}} = y, \; \frac{\partial y}{\partial \bar{y}} = y_2, \ldots$$

To compute the increments of  $x_1, x_2, y_1, y_2, \ldots$  under the
infinitesimal transformation  B,  we form the equations

$$\delta(dx - x_1 d\bar{x} - x_2 d\bar{y}) = 0, \qquad \delta(dy - y_1 d\bar{x} - y_2 d\bar{y}) = 0 .$$

Using the abbreviations  $\partial F/\partial x = F_x$,  $\partial F/\partial y = F_y$,  this
gives us

---

[*]  Möbius dealt incidentally with this infinite group.
(Crelles Journal Vol. XII).

$$x_1 = (X_x x_1 + X_y y_1)\delta t \quad,$$

$$x_2 = (X_x x_2 + X_y y_2)\delta t \quad,$$

$$y_1 = (Y_x x_1 + Y_y y_1)\delta t \quad,$$

$$y_2 = (Y_x x_2 + Y_y y_2)\delta t \quad.$$

<u>Hence</u> $x, y, x_1, x_2, y_1, y_2$ <u>are transformed by an infinite group with the infinitesimal transformations</u>

$$X \frac{\partial}{\partial x} + Y \frac{\partial}{\partial y} + (X_x x_1 + X_y y_1)\frac{\partial}{\partial x_1} + (X_x x_2 + X_y y_2)\frac{\partial}{\partial x_2}$$

$$+ (Y_x x_1 + Y_y y_1)\frac{\partial}{\partial y_1} + (Y_x x_2 + Y_y y_2)\frac{\partial}{\partial y_2} = B' \quad.$$

In this one must remember that $X$ and $Y$ are subject to the sole relation $X_x + Y_y = 0$. Now if there are functions of $x, y$ and their <u>first</u> derivatives which admit this group, they must satisfy all the equations $B'f = 0$, or, equivalently, the five equations

$$\left.\begin{aligned}
\frac{\partial f}{\partial x} &= 0 \\
\frac{\partial f}{\partial y} &= 0 \\
x_1\frac{\partial f}{\partial x_1} + x_2\frac{\partial f}{\partial x_2} - y_1\frac{\partial f}{\partial y_1} - y_2\frac{\partial f}{\partial y_2} &= 0 \\
y_1\frac{\partial f}{\partial x_1} + y_2\frac{\partial f}{\partial x_2} &= 0 \\
x_1\frac{\partial f}{\partial y_1} + x_2\frac{\partial f}{\partial y_2} &= 0
\end{aligned}\right\} \quad (4.3.1)$$

It can be verified in the familiar way that these five
equations form a complete system. This can also be seen
as follows.

Since $X$ and $Y$ are related by $X_x + Y_y = 0$,
there is a function of $x$ and $y$ whose first derivatives
are $X$ and $-Y$ respectively. Hence if we take two
arbitrary infinitesimal transformations $B$, they are of
the form

$$B_1 = \frac{\partial U}{\partial y} \frac{\partial}{\partial x} - \frac{\partial U}{\partial x} \frac{\partial}{\partial y} \quad ,$$

$$B_2 = \frac{\partial V}{\partial y} \frac{\partial}{\partial x} - \frac{\partial V}{\partial x} \frac{\partial}{\partial y} \quad .$$

Direct computation gives

$$[B_1,B_2] = \frac{\partial (U_y V_x - U_x V_y)}{\partial y} \frac{\partial}{\partial \overline{x}} - \frac{\partial (U_y V_x - U_x V_y)}{\partial x} \frac{\partial}{\partial \overline{y}} \quad ,$$

so that $[B_1,B_2]$ does possess the general form $B$ in
agreement with Theorem 4.1.2. Therefore, if, in the general
expression of the infinitesimal transformation $B'$, one
first puts $X = U_y$, $Y = -U_x$ and then $X = V_y$, $Y = -V_x$,
one obtains the two expressions $B_1',B_2'$, and one verifies
easily that $[B_1',B_2']$ is of the form $B'$. From this it
follows that the five equations (4.3.1), which are equivalent to all the equations $B'f = 0$, do form a complete
system. Therefore, the solution of the system, namely

$$I = x_1 y_2 - x_2 y_1 \quad ,$$

is the unique first-order differential invariant of the
group.

Since the independent variables $\bar{x}, \bar{y}$ of our group
are not transformed, it is clear that all the derivatives
of I with respect to $\bar{x}$ and $\bar{y}$ are themselves invariants; and since these derivatives cannot be connected by
any relation, we see that the group has (at least) two
differential invariants of order two, three of order three,
and in general n invariants of order n.

That there are these many invariants of orders
$2,3,\ldots,n$ can be seen by setting up their defining equations. For, x,y and their four first derivatives and
six second derivatives are transformed by an infinite group
whose infinitesimal transformations are of the form

$$B'' = X \frac{\partial}{\partial x} + Y \frac{\partial}{\partial y} + X_x A_1 + X_y A_2 + Y_x A_3 + Y_y A_4 + X_{xx} A_5$$

$$+ X_{yx} A_6 + X_{yy} A_7 + Y_{xx} A_8 + Y_{xy} A_9 + Y_{yy} A_{10} \quad .$$

In this the $A_k$ are determining operators, which are
completely independent of the form of the arbitrary functions X,Y. Using the relations

$$X_x + Y_y = 0, \quad X_{xx} + Y_{xy} = 0, \quad X_{xy} + Y_{yy} = 0 ,$$

one sees that the totality of equations $B''f = 0$ is equivalent to the nine equations

$$\frac{\partial f}{\partial x} = 0, \qquad \frac{\partial f}{\partial y} = 0, \qquad A_1 f - A_4 f = 0,$$

$$A_2 f = 0, \qquad A_3 f = 0, \qquad A_5 f - A_9 f = 0,$$

$$A_6 f - A_{10} f = 0, \qquad A_7 f = 0, \qquad A_8 f = 0,$$

which form a complete system with <u>three</u> solutions. Among
these one is of first order, namely  J,  while the two
others are of second order.  By analogous reasoning one
can show the existence of three third order invariants,
and so on.

Our infinite group determines still other sequences
of invariants, which will be indicated here briefly.

To the variables  x  and  y,  which are transformed
by the group, adjoin <u>three</u> new quantities  $\bar{x}, \bar{y}, \bar{z}$  invariant
under the group, and consider  x,y  as functions of  $\bar{x}, \bar{y}, \bar{z}$.
Then  x,y  and their derivatives are transformed by an
infinite group.  One finds three first-order invariants

$$\frac{\partial x}{\partial \bar{x}} \frac{\partial y}{\partial \bar{y}} - \frac{\partial x}{\partial \bar{y}} \frac{\partial y}{\partial \bar{x}} \qquad ,$$

$$\frac{\partial x}{\partial \bar{x}} \frac{\partial y}{\partial \bar{z}} - \frac{\partial x}{\partial \bar{z}} \frac{\partial y}{\partial \bar{x}} \qquad ,$$

$$\frac{\partial x}{\partial \bar{y}} \frac{\partial y}{\partial \bar{z}} - \frac{\partial x}{\partial \bar{z}} \frac{\partial y}{\partial \bar{y}} \qquad ,$$

eight essential second-order invariants, and so on.


*COMMENTS*

   *This is very interesting material because it illus-*
*trates certain general ideas.*

   *Let   X   and   Z   be manifolds, and let*

        $M(X,Z)$

*be the space of maps*

        $\phi: X \to Z$   .

*Let   $M^r(X,Z)$   be (as in Chapter A) the space of* r*-th order*
*mapping elements, the quotient of*

        $X \times M(X,Z)$

*by a certain equivalence relations.   (In the example dis-*
*cussed by Lie in this section,*

        $Z$ = *space of variables*   $(x,y)$
        $X$ = *space of variables*   $(\overline{x},\overline{y})$   .)

   *Suppose   G   is a group of diffeomorphisms acting on*
Z   *alone.   (This is what Lie means when he says that "the*
*variables   $(\overline{x},\overline{y})$   are not transformed by the group".)   G*
*acts on   $M(X,Z)$   and   $X \times M(X,Z)$   as follows*

        $g(\phi)(x)$   =   $g(\phi(x))$
        *for*   $g \in G$,   $\phi \in M(X,Z)$,   $x \in X$

$$g(x,\phi) = (gx, g\phi)$$

$G$, *acting in this way, passes to the quotient to act on*

$$M^r(X,Z) \quad .$$

*Now, <u>assume</u> that $\omega$ is a differential form on $Z$ which is invariant under $G$. (In the text,*

$$\omega = dx \wedge dy \quad .$$

$G$ *is <u>defined</u> as the group of diffeomorphisms which preserves this form. Cartan later, in his work on Infinite Lie Groups, showed that <u>every</u> such group could be defined as the group of all diffeomorphisms of some manifold preserving a collection of differential forms.)*

*Suppose that $\omega$ is a p-th degree differential form. Let*

$$\Lambda^p T^d(X)$$

*denote the vector bundle over $X$, whose fiber over a point $x \in X$ is the space of p-th degree skew-symmetric multilinear form on the tangent space $X_x$. $\omega$ now defines a mapping*

$$\bar{\omega}: X \times M(X,Z) \to \Lambda^p T^d(X)$$

*as follows:*

$$\bar{\omega}(x,\phi) = \phi^*(\omega)(x)$$

*If $r=1$, this map passes to the quotient with respect to the equivalence relation defining $M^1(X,Z)$,* *to define a map*

$$\overline{\omega}: M^1(X,Z) \to \Lambda^p T^d(X)$$

*This map obviously (because* G *leaves invariant* ω*)*
*intertwines the action of* G*. But,* G *acts as the iden-*
*tity on* $\Lambda^p T^d(X)$*.* $\overline{\omega}$ *is a first order differential invari-*
*ant, in the sense of Lie, when suitably specialized, (e.g.,*
*by choosing coordinates* $(\overline{x},\overline{y})$ *for* X *and writing* $\overline{\omega}$
*in terms of the coordinates for* $\Lambda^p T^d(X)$*.)*

  *One can now iterate the construction to obtain higher*
*order differential invariants. Suppose, for example, that*

$$p = 2 \quad,$$

*i.e.,* ω *is a two-form. As explained in Volume IX,* ω
*determines a two-form, denoted by*

$$\dot{\omega}$$

*on* $T(Z)$*. (*ω *defines a map* $T(Z) \to T^d(Z)$*. Let* θ *be the*
*homogeneous contact one-form on* $T^d(Z)$*. Pull back* θ
*under this map, and call it* ω*.) Let* G *act--via its*
*natural "prolongation" to tangent vectors--on* $T(Z)$*.*

   G *leaves* $\dot{\omega}$ *invariant*

*Hence, there is a map*

$$\overline{\omega}: X \times M(X,Z) \to \Lambda^2 T^d(T(Z))$$

*which intertwines* G *defined as follows:*

$$\bar{\omega}(x,\phi) \;\; = \;\; (\phi_*)^*(\dot{\omega})(x)$$

$\bar{\omega}$ *passes to the quotient to define a (fiber preserving)*
*map*

$$M^2(X,Z) \;\to\; \Lambda^2 T^d(T(Z))$$

*This map is a* _second order differential invariant_ *under the*
*action of* G.

*Much the same process will work when* $\omega$ *is replaced*
*by an* _arbitrary tensor field on_ Z.

## 4.4    A GENERAL PROCEDURE FOR PROVING EXISTENCE OF DIFFERENTIAL INVARIANTS

We now want to prove the existence of differential
invariants for any infinite group.  Suppose the variables
$x,y,\ldots,u,v,\ldots$  are transformed by an infinite group

$$x_1 \;\; = \;\; F(x,y,\ldots,u,v,\ldots) \quad ,$$

$$y_1 \;\; = \;\; \Phi(x,y,\ldots,u,v,\ldots) \quad ,$$

Let  $z,w,\ldots$  be quantities invariant under the group.  It
is then obvious that the combined equations

$$x_1 = F, \;\; y_1 = \Phi,\ldots, \; z_1 = z, \; w_1 = w,\ldots \qquad (4.4.2)$$

form an infinite group.  The infinitesimal transformations
of this new group have the form

$$B \;\; = \;\; X\,\frac{\partial}{\partial x} + Y\,\frac{\partial}{\partial y} + Z\,\frac{\partial}{\partial z} + \cdots + U\,\frac{\partial}{\partial u} + V\,\frac{\partial}{\partial v} + W\,\frac{\partial}{\partial w} + \cdots$$

In this, Z and W are zero, while X,Y,...,U,V,...
depend only on x,y,...,u,v,... and are determined as
functions of these by the defining equations of the group

$$0 = A_i X + B_i Y + \cdots + L_i X_x + M_i X_y + \cdots \quad (4.4.2)$$

If we consider u,v,w,... as functions of x,y,z,...
as in Section 3.3 and write

$$\frac{\partial^{m+n+p+\cdots} F}{\partial x^m \partial y^n \partial z^p \cdots} = F_{m,n,p,\ldots} \quad ,$$

then the derivatives

$$u_{m,n,p,\ldots}, \quad v_{m,n,p,\ldots}, \quad w_{m,n,p,\ldots}$$

are transformed in accordance with formulas (4.4.1).

First, it is clear that x,y,z,..., u,v,w,... and
their <u>first</u> derivatives are transformed by a certain infinite
group. The infinitesimal transformations B' of this group
are found by introducing the values of the increments

$$\delta u_{m,n,p,\ldots}, \quad \delta v_{m,n,p,\ldots}, \quad \delta w_{m,n,p,\ldots}, \quad \cdots$$

in the formula

$$B' = B + \sum_{m+n+p+\cdots=1} \frac{\delta u_{m,n,p,\ldots}}{\delta t} \cdot \frac{\partial}{\partial u_{m,n,p,\ldots}}$$

$$+ \sum_{m+n+p+\cdots=1} \frac{\delta v_{m,n,p,\ldots}}{\delta t} \cdot \frac{\partial}{\partial v_{m,n,p,\ldots}} + \cdots$$

These increments, which are calculated by the rules of the
calculus of variations, are obviously <u>linear</u> functions of
X,Y,...,U,V,... and their <u>first</u> derivatives with respect
to x,y,...,u,v,... .

Next, it is clear that x,y,z,...,u,v,w,... and
their <u>first</u> and <u>second</u> derivatives are transformed by an
infinite group. Its infinitesimal transformations B" are
of the form

$$B'' = B' + \sum_{m+n+p+\cdots=2} \frac{\delta u_{m,n,p,\ldots}}{\delta t} \cdot \frac{\partial}{\partial u_{m,n,p,\ldots}}$$

$$+ \sum_{m+n+p+\cdots=2} \frac{\delta v_{m,n,p,\ldots}}{\delta t} \cdot \frac{\partial}{\partial v_{m,n,p,\ldots}} +\cdots ,$$

where the increments $\delta u_{m,n,p,\ldots}$ are linear functions of
X,Y,...,U,V,... and their first and second derivatives with
respect to x,y,...,u,v,... .

In the same way one can form the general expressions
of $B^{(3)},B^{(4)},\ldots,B^{(q)}$, where $B^{(q)}$ is the general infinitesimal transformation of an infinite group connecting
x,y,z,...,u,v,w,... and the derivatives of orders 1,2,...,q.
These $B^{(q)}$ have the form

$$B^{(q)} = X \frac{\partial}{\partial x} + Y \frac{\partial}{\partial y} +\cdots+ U \frac{\partial}{\partial u} + V \frac{\partial}{\partial v} +\cdots+$$

$$+ X_x A_1 + X_y A_2 + X_u A_3 + X_v A_4 +\cdots+$$

$$+ V_x C_1 + V_y C_2 + V_u C_3 + V_v C_4 +\cdots+ X_{xx} D_1 +\cdots .$$

Here the operators $A_k, C_k, D_k, \ldots$ are completely independent of the functions $X, Y, \ldots, U, V, \ldots$ . This expression for $B^{(q)}$ can be simplified. By means of the defining equations (4.4.2) and the relations that follow from them by differentiation, some of the quantities

$$X, Y, \ldots, U, V, \ldots, X_x, \ldots, X_{xx}, \ldots$$

can be eliminated from the expression for $B^{(q)}$; in fact, in general one can arrange that the number $\nu$ of those quantities of the above list which remain in $B^{(q)}$ is less than the number $\mu$ of the quantities $x, y, z, \ldots, u, v, w, \ldots$ and the appropriate derivatives of orders $1, 2, \ldots, q$.

This is always possible because $q$ can be chosen arbitrarily large and in any particular case we can introduce as many quantities $z, w, \ldots$ invariant under the group as we wish.

Assuming that $\nu < \mu$, the totality of <u>all</u> equations of the form $B^{(q)}f = 0$ is equivalent to $\nu$ linear first-order partial differential equations with $\mu$ independent variables. These $\nu$ equations form a complete system with (at least) $\mu - \nu$ solutions; this is a simple consequence of Theorem 4.1.2. It follows from what has gone before that the solutions of the complete system are differential invariants of order $q$ of our group. This proves the following theorem.

Theorem 4.4.1.  <u>Every infinite continuous group determines</u>
<u>an infinite sequence of differential invariants</u>, <u>which can</u>
<u>be defined as the solutions of complete systems</u>.

If a system of differential equations of order  q
admits our infinite group, then in general that system can
be written in the form of finitely many relations among the
differential invariants of order  $\leq q$.  If this is not the
case, the differential equations can be determined by simple
considerations in any particular case.  I shall not go into
this further now.  On the other hand I explicitly state
that if one has found sufficiently many differential invariants, then arbitrarily many can be computed by <u>differentia-</u>
<u>tion</u>.  The new invariants are found by division of Jacobian
determinants.

We now give a large number of examples of the preceding theory.


*COMMENTS ON SECTION 4*

*Here is the general setting.  Let*  X,Z  *be manifolds,*
*as usual in these Comments.  Let*

$$\underset{\sim}{G} \subset V(X \times Z)$$

*be a Lie algebra of vector fields on*  X × Z.  *Suppose it is*
*defined by differential equations, in the sense that there*

*is a collection*

$$D_1, \ldots, D_s : V(X \times Z) \to F(X \times Z)$$

*of linear differential operators such that:*

$$\underset{\sim}{G} = \{ A \varepsilon V(X \times Z): D_1(A) = 0 = \cdots = D_s(A) \}$$

*Now, construct*

$$M^r(X, Z) \quad ,$$

*and let* $\underset{\sim}{G}$ *act on* $M^r(X, Z)$ *via its natural geometric prolongation. (See Chapter A.) Lie states that, if* r *is sufficiently large, the orbits of* $\underset{\sim}{G}$ *on* $M^r(X, Z)$ *are of lower dimension than the dimension of* $M^r(X, Z)$ *itself. In particular, there are (at least locally in the neighborhood of the maximal orbits) functions*

$$\Omega : M^r(X, Z) \to R$$

*which are solutions of the "complete" linear differential equation system*

$$A^r(\Omega) = 0$$
$$for \ all \quad A \ \varepsilon \ \underset{\sim}{G}$$

*These are the <u>differential invariants</u>.*

   *As far as I can tell, Lie (in the spirit of the 18-th century) assumes that everything is suitably "general", and that these facts are self evident. As far as I know, they are not proved to this day!*

## 4.5     DIFFERENTIAL INVARIANTS OF SECONDARY, ORDINARY
DIFFERENTIAL EQUATIONS

I consider an arbitrary second-order differential
equation of the form

$$y'' = \Phi(x,y,y') \quad .$$

Replace  y  and  x  by new variables  $y_1, x_1$  via a substitution

$$y_1 = Y(x,y), \qquad x_1 = X(x,y) \quad . \qquad (4.5.1)$$

Then

$$y_1' = \frac{Y_x + Y_y y'}{X_x + X_y y'} \qquad (4.5.2)$$

and

$$y_1'' = \frac{Ay'' + Bu'^3 + Cy'^2 + Dy' + E}{(X_x + X_y y')^3} \quad ;$$

here  A,B,C,D,E  denote certain functions of  x,y  which
can not be written down explicitly.

When written in the new variables  $x_1, y_1$  the equation  $y'' - \Phi = 0$  assumes the form  $y_1'' - \Phi_1 = 0$,  where

$$\Phi_1 = \frac{A\Phi + By'^3 + Cy'^2 + Dy' + E}{(X_x + X_y y')^3} \quad . \qquad (4.5.3)$$

It is now obvious that Equations 4.5.1, 4.5.2, 4.5.3 determine an infinite group of transformations of $x, y, y', \Phi$, considering these as four independent quantities. By our general theorem this group has several infinite sequences of differential invariants. However, we need only consider those invariants which correspond to the exceptional case where $\Phi$ is a function $x$, $y$ and $y'$.

We first compute the infinitesimal transformations of the group. Setting

$$\delta x = \xi(x,y)\delta t, \qquad \delta y = \eta(x,y)\delta t,$$

one has

$$\frac{\delta y'}{\delta t} = \eta_x + y'(\eta_y - \xi_x) - y'^2 \xi_y = \zeta,$$

$$\frac{\delta \Phi}{\delta t} = (\eta_y - 2\xi_x - 3y'\xi_y)\Phi - y'^2(\eta_{yy} - 2\xi_{xy})$$

$$+ y'(2\eta_{xy} - \xi_{xx}) + \eta_{xx} = \phi \qquad (4.5.4)$$

and

$$B = \xi \frac{\partial}{\partial x} + \eta \frac{\partial}{\partial y} + \zeta \frac{\partial}{\partial y'} + \phi \frac{\partial}{\partial \Phi} \quad .$$

We compute the increments of $\Phi_x$, $\Phi_y$, $\Phi_{y'}$ by the calculus of variations and put

$$B' = B + \frac{\delta \Phi_x}{\delta t} \frac{\partial}{\partial \Phi_x} + \frac{\delta \Phi_y}{\delta t} \frac{\partial}{\partial \Phi_y} + \frac{\delta \Phi_{y'}}{\delta t} \frac{\partial}{\partial \Phi_{y'}} \quad .$$

Note that $B'$ is linear and homogeneous with respect to $\xi, \eta$ and their derivatives of order $\leq 3$. Further, the defining Equations 4.5.4 of our group enable us to eliminate $\zeta$ and $\phi$ from the expressions for $B$ and $B'$. One computes $B'', \ldots, B^{(q)}$ in a completely analogous way, and one sees from this, as before, the general existence of differential invariants of our gorup.

Hence every ordinary second-order differential equation of the form

$$y'' - \Phi(x, y, y') = 0$$

determines infinitely many invariants

$$\Omega(y', \Phi, \Phi_x, \Phi_y, \Phi_{y'}, \Phi_{x,x}, \ldots)$$

of the group of all point-transformations.

We shall indicate how one can find covariants of the equations

$$y'' - \Phi(x, y, y') = 0$$

with respect to the group of all point-transformations. Put

$$B' + \frac{\delta y'''}{\delta t} \frac{\partial}{\partial y'''} = C' \quad ,$$

and compute $\delta y'''$ in the usual way as a <u>linear</u> function of $\xi, \eta$ and their derivatives of order $\leq 3$. In the resulting expression replace $y''$ by $\Phi$. Then the $C'$ are the infinitesimal transformations of an infinite group.

Now put

$$B'' + \frac{\delta y}{\delta t} \frac{\partial}{\partial y} + \frac{\delta y^{(4)}}{\delta t} \frac{\partial}{\partial y^{(4)}} = C'' \quad ,$$

and again replace $y''$ throughout by $\Phi$. Then the $C''$ are also the infinitesimal transformations of an infinite group. If one computes $C^{(3)}, \ldots, C^{(q)}$ in the same way and chooses $q$ sufficiently large, then the equations $C^{(q)} f = 0$ form a complete system. Its solutions are of the form

$$W(y', y''', \ldots, y^{(q+2)}, \Phi, \Phi_x, \Phi_y, \Phi_{y'}, \Phi_{x,x}, \ldots)$$

and are invariant under all point-transformations.[*] It is clear that a completely analogous computation will yield all invariants (or covariants) of the equation $y'' - \Phi = 0$ with respect to an arbitrary infinite (or finite) group of point-transformations.

---

[*] Note that in computing the covariants of the equation $y'' - \Phi = 0$ it is not necessary to eliminate $y''$.

*COMMENTS ON SECTION 5*

*Here we begin development of ideas that are extremely
important and completely lost to modern mathematics.   In
the rest of the paper Lie develops a very general differential-
geometric method for constructing the "covariants" of a
geometric object.   This material was carried on to a certain
extent by E. Cartan (with what he calls the "method of the
moving frame"), but not in Lie's direct way.   I believe
that understanding these ideas better will be very important
for physics and engineering.*

*Here is the general procedure covering the material
of this section (and much of the later sections as well).
Let  X  and  Z  be manifolds,  $\underset{\sim}{G}$  a Lie algebra of vector
fields on  X × Z  which is defined by differential equations.*

*$\underset{\sim}{G}$  may be prolonged to act on a Lie algebra of vector
fields on*

$$M^r(X,Z)  .$$

*For each integer  m  and  s,   consider*

$$C^s(M^n(X,Z),m)   ,$$

*the <u>contact manifold of</u> r-<u>order</u> elements of m-dimensional
submanifolds of  $M^n(X,Z)$.  $\underset{\sim}{G}$,  acting on  $M^r(X,Z)$  can be
prolonged to act on*

$$C^s(M^r(X,Z),m)   .$$

*Differential invariants of differential equations (relative to* $G$*) are functions on* $C^S(M^r(X,Z),m)$ *which are invariant under* $G$.

    *Recall that a* <u>*differential equation*</u> *is a submanifold of* $M^r(X,Z)$.   *Say, that it is parameterized as follows.*

$$\alpha: Y \to M^r(X,Z) \quad ,$$

*where* $Y$ *is a manifold of dimension* $m$.   *(In the example of this section,*

      $Y$ *is the space of variables* $(x,y,y')$

      $M^r(X,Z)$ *is the space of variables* $(x,y,y',y'')$

$\alpha$ *is the following map:*

$$\alpha(x,y,y') = (x,y,y',y'' = \Phi(x,y,y')))$$

*Then, let*

$$\partial\alpha: Y \to C^S(M^r(X,Z),m)$$

*be the prolongation of* $\alpha$.  *If* $\Omega$ *is a differential variant,*

$$(\partial\alpha)^*(\Omega)$$

*is the* <u>*basic object Lie considers in this section.*</u>  *(For example, he denotes it by*

$$\Omega(x,y,y',\Phi,\Phi_x,\Phi_y,\dots) \quad .)$$

## 4.6    DIFFERENTIAL INVARIANTS OF POINT TRANSFORMATIONS

We shall now show that an expression of the form $W(x,y,y')$ has invariants (and covariants) with respect to all point-transformations.  As we know, under the infinitesimal point-transformation

$$\xi(x,y)\ \frac{\partial}{\partial x} + \eta(x,y)\ \frac{\partial}{\partial y}\quad,$$

$y'$ receives the increment

$$\frac{\delta y'}{\delta t}\ =\ \eta_x + (\eta_y - \xi_x)y' - \xi_y y'^2\ =\ \zeta\quad.$$

Hence

$$B'\ =\ \xi\ \frac{\partial}{\partial x} + \eta\ \frac{\partial}{\partial y} + \zeta\ \frac{\partial}{\partial y'}$$

is the general infinitesimal transformation of the infinite group

$$y_1\ =\ Y(x,y),\quad x_1\ =\ X(x,y),\quad y_1'\ =\ \frac{Y_x + Y_y y'}{X_x + X_y y'}$$

$$(4.6.1)$$

Introducing new variables $x_1, y_1, y_1'$ in $W(x,y,y')$ changes it to the new form $W_1(x_1,y_1,y_1')$, where

$$W(x,y,y')\ =\ W_1(x_1,y_1,y_1')\quad,$$

and therefore  W  must be considered an invariant of the group (4.6.1).

On the other hand, the derivatives of W with respect to $x, y, y'$ change not only their form under a transformation (4.6.1) but also their <u>value</u>. One computes the increments

$$\delta W_x, \delta W_y, \delta W_{y'}, \delta W_{xx}, \ldots$$

as usual, and thus sees the existence of invariants

$$\Omega(y', W_x, W_y, W_{y'}, \ldots)$$

and covariants

$$\Phi(y', y'', y, \ldots, W_x, W_y, W_{y'}, \ldots) \quad,$$

which, as always, are defined as solutions of complete systems.


4.7    CONTINUATION

Again consider the infinite group of all point-transformations

$$y_1 = Y(x,y), \qquad x_1 = X(x,y) \quad.$$

Replacing the variables $x, y$ of three functions $f$, $F$ and $\Phi$ by new variables $x_1, y_1$ changes the form of these functions to $f_1$, $F_1$ and $\Phi_1$ but does not change their value. Hence I consider $f$, $F$ and $\Phi$ as invariants of our infinite group. On the other hand, the derivatives

$f_x, f_y, F_x, F_y, \Phi_x, \Phi_y$  are transformed, and one easily sees the
existence of invariants of the form

$$I(f_x, f_y, F_x, F_y, \Phi_x, \Phi_y, \ldots)$$

since  $y', y'', \ldots$  are also transformed by our group, there
are also invariants of the form

$$\Omega(f_x, f_y, \ldots, \Phi_y, \ldots, y', y'', \ldots) \quad .$$

Noting that the equations  $f$ = const.,  $F$ = const.,
$\Phi$ = const.  determine three families of curves and that the
(fourth) family of the curves which intersect these with
constant anharmonic cross-ratio is determined by a <u>first</u>-
order differential equation, one finds, without computation,
an invariant  $\Omega$  which depends only on the four quantities
$f_x/f_y$,  $F_x/F_y$,  $\Phi_x/\Phi_y$,  $y'$.


## 4.8    HIGHER ORDER ORDINARY DIFFERENTIAL EQUATIONS

An ordinary differential equation of order  $\geq 3$,
$$y^{(n)} - \Phi(x, y, y', \ldots, y^{(n-1)}) = 0$$

has invariants and covariants not only with respect to all
point-transformations but also with respect to all contact-
transformations.  And two or more differential equations
have simultaneous invariants or covariants.  Similarly,
expressions of the form  $\Phi(x, y, y', \ldots, y^{(m)})$  determine invariants and covariants.

## 4.9    INVARIANTS OF A SECOND ORDER, NON-LINEAR EQUATION

In an equation of the form

$$0 = y'' + F_3(x,y)y'^3 + F_2(x,y)y'^2 + F_1 y' + F \quad ,$$

introduce new variables

$$y_1 = Y(x,y), \qquad x_1 = X(x,y) \quad ;$$

this yields a new equation of the analogous form

$$0 = y_1'' + \Phi_3(x_1,y_1)y_1'^3 + \Phi_2(x_1,y_1)y_1'^2 + \Phi_1 y_1' + \quad ,$$

where the $\Phi_k$ are functions of the $F_i$ and on $X, Y$ and their derivatives:

$$\Phi_k = \Pi_k(F_3, F_2, F_1, F, X_x, X_y, \dots) \quad ;$$

and these last equations, taken together with $y_1 = Y$, $x_1 = X$, determine an infinite group.

To find the invariants of this group we first compute the $\delta\Phi_k$ as follows.  In the equation

$$\delta y'' + \delta y'(3F_3 y'^2 + 2F_2 y' + F_1) + \delta F_3 y'^3 + \delta F_2 y'^2 + \delta F_1 y' + \delta F = 0$$

introduce the values

$$\delta y' = \eta_x + (\eta_y - \xi_x)y' - \xi_y y'^2 \quad ,$$

$$\delta y'' = (\eta_y - 2\xi_x - 3\xi_y y')y'' - \xi_{yy} y'^3 + (\eta_{yy} - 2\xi_{xy})y'^2$$

$$+ (2\eta_{xy} - \xi_{xx})y' + \eta_{xx} \quad ,$$

then eliminate $y''$ and require that the resulting equations
hold identically with respect to $y'$. This yields a determination of the $\delta F_k$, and we see that there are invariants
of the form

$$\Omega(F, F_1, F_2, F_3, F_x, F_y, \ldots) \quad .$$

## 4.10  A GROUP ACTING ON A SPECIAL TYPE OF SECOND ORDER, ORDINARY DIFFERENTIAL EQUATION

In the equation

$$y'' - F(x,y) = 0$$

introduce new variables of the form

$$x_1 = \Phi(x), \qquad y_1 = cy\sqrt{\Phi'(x)} + \Pi(x) \qquad (4.10.1)$$

one easily verifies that this gives a new equation of the
analogous form

$$y_1'' - F_1(x_1, y_1) = 0 \quad ,$$

where $F_1$ is a function of $F$, $\Phi$, $c$ and $\Pi$:

$$F_1 = f(F, \Phi, \Pi, c) \quad . \qquad\qquad (4.10.2)$$

Since the Equations 4.10.1 and 4.10.2 taken together.
Therefore, the equation $y'' - F(x,y) = 0$ has invariants
of the form

$$\Omega(F, F_x, F_y, \ldots) \quad .$$

*COMMENTS ON SECTION 10*

*This is a very interesting example. Here, one is*
*investigating invariance with respect to a* <u>*subgroup*</u> *G*
*of the group of all diffeomorphisms of* (x,y)-*space, namely*
*the subgroup defined by Equations 4.10.1. Let us investi-*
*gate the differential geometric meaning of this group*

*If* $\Phi(x)$, $\Pi(x)$ *are functions of* x, *let*

$$\alpha: R^2 \to R^2$$

*be the diffeomorphism defined as follows:*

$$\alpha(x,y) = (\Phi(x), y\sqrt{\Phi'(x)} + \Pi(x))$$

*Then,*

$$\alpha^*(x) = \Phi(x)$$

$$\alpha^*(y) = y\sqrt{\Phi'} + \Pi$$

*Hence,*

$$\alpha^*(dx \wedge dy) = \Phi' dx \wedge (d(y\sqrt{\Phi'} + \Pi)$$

$$= (\Phi')^{3/2} dx \wedge dy$$

*Consider the fiber space projection map*

$$R^2 \to R$$

*defined by assigning*

$$(x,y) \to x \quad .$$

G  *consists of the* <u>*fiber space automorphisms of*</u>  $R^2$  <u>*such*</u>
<u>*that*</u>

$$\alpha^*(dx \wedge dy) = f(x)dx \wedge dy \quad ,$$

*for some function*  f  *of*  x  *alone. This group admits*
*higher dimensional generalizations, which have never really*
*been investigated.*


4.11   DIFFERENTIAL INVARIANTS OF SECOND ORDER PARTIAL
       DIFFERENTIAL EQUATIONS

In the second-order partial differential equation

$$r = F(x,y,z,p,q,s,t)$$

introduce new variables

$$x_1 = X(x,y,z), \qquad y_1 = Y(x,y,z), \qquad z_1 = Z(x,y,z)$$

$$(4.11.1)$$

to get an equation

$$r_1 = F_1(x_1,y_1,z_1,p_1,q_1,s_1,t_1) \quad ,$$

where  $p_1$, $q_1$, $s_1$, $t_1$  and  $F_1$  are functions of  $p,q,s,t,F$
and of  X,Y,Z  and their first and second derivatives:

$$p_1 = P, \quad q_1 = Q, \quad s_1 = S, \quad t_1 = T, \quad F_1 = \Phi \quad (4.11.2)$$

Now since the equations (4.11.1), (4.11.2) must define an
infinite group, the equation  $r - F = 0$  determines infinitely
many differential invariants of the form

$$\Omega(p,q,s,t,F,F_x,F_y,\ldots,F_t,\ldots) \quad .$$

To compute these invariants one must first set up the infinitesimal transformations of the group. One begins with the infinitesimal transformation

$$\xi(x,y,z) \frac{\partial}{\partial x} + \eta \frac{\partial}{\partial y} + \zeta \frac{\partial}{\partial z} \quad ,$$

computes the corresponding increments of $p,q,r,s,t,$ and then replaces $r$ everywhere by $F$. Then one determines the increments

$$\delta F_x, \delta F_y, \ldots, \delta F_t$$

by <u>variation</u> of the equation

$$dF - F_x dx - F_y dy - F_z dz - F_p dp - F_q dq - F_s ds - F_t dt = 0 ,$$

and then continues in the usual way.

I announced as early as 1872 that partial differential equations of arbitrary order determine invariants with respect to all point-transformations and with respect to all contact-transformations.

By taking sufficiently many invariants $J_1, J_2, \ldots, J_8$ of a <u>given</u> equation $r-F = 0$ and computing them as functions of $x,y,z,p,q,s,t,$ it is always possible to derive relations of the form

$$\Pi(J_1, J_2, \ldots, J_8, \ldots) = 0$$

by elimination.

   This is the basis for a rational classification of
all the partial differential equations  r-F = 0,  and
obviously this remark extends to arbitrary partial differential equations (Göttinger Nachr. 1872, p. 479 [Collected
Papers Vol. III, paper IV, p. 20, lines 3-1 from the bottom]).

   If several functions of  x,y,z,p,q,r,s,t  are given,
these obviously determine simultaneous invariants and covariants of the groups of all point- or all contact-
transformations.


*COMMENTS*

   *First, we must give an explanation of the notations
used in this section.  Lie does not define what "p,q,r,s,t"
are, because they involve standard notation in the mathematics of his day.  If  (x,y) → z(x,y)  defines a surface
in  $R^3$, then  "p,q,r,s,t" denotes the partial derivatives
of the function  z(x,y). Here is a precise explanation in
terms of the notation of Chapter A.*

   *Let*

      $X = R^2 \equiv$ *space of variables*  (x,y)

      $Z = R$  = *space of variables*  z.

*Then*

$$M(X,Z) = \textit{space of mappings}$$

$$(x,y) \rightarrow z(x,y) \quad \textit{of} \quad X \rightarrow Z$$

*i.e.,*

$$M(X,Z) \equiv F(X) \quad .$$

*However, what is most important for* geometry *is to identify* $M(X,Z)$ *with the space of* surfaces *in* $R^3$. *In fact:*

$$X \times Z \equiv R^2 \times R \equiv R^3$$

$$= \textit{space of variables} \quad (x,y,z) \quad .$$

*Hence, the "graph" mapping*

$$\textit{graph}: M(X,Z) \rightarrow SM(X \times Z)$$

*embeds* $M(X,Z)$ *as a subspaceof the space of submanifolds of* $R^3$. *It is this correspondence that is obviously of the most importance for the classical differential geometry of surfaces in* $R^3$. *(This is why Lie takes it for granted that his readers know what* "p,q,r,s,t" *mean! I am sure that not a mathematician alive today understands this notation, unless he is familiar with the 19-th century differential geometry literature.)*

*Here is how I would define* "p,q,r,s,t" as functions on $M^2(X,Z)$. *Denote an element of* $M(X,Z)$ *by*

$$\overline{z} \quad .$$

*(Thus,* $\overline{z}$ *means a function* $(x,y) \rightarrow \overline{z}(x,y).)$ *Define functions*

$$\overline{p},\overline{q},\overline{r},\overline{s},\overline{t}: X \times M(X,Z) \rightarrow R$$

*by the following formulas:*

$$\overline{p}((x,y),\overline{z}) \quad = \quad \frac{\partial \overline{z}}{\partial x}\,(x,y)$$

$$\overline{q}((x,y),\overline{z}) \quad = \quad \frac{\partial \overline{z}}{\partial y}\,(x,y)$$

$$\overline{r}((x,y),\overline{z}) \quad = \quad \frac{\partial^2 \overline{z}}{\partial x^2}\,(x,y)$$

$$\overline{s}((x,y),\overline{z}) \quad = \quad \frac{\partial^2 \overline{z}}{\partial x \partial y}\,(x,y)$$

$$\overline{t}((x,y),\overline{z}) \quad = \quad \frac{\partial^2 \overline{z}}{\partial y^2}\,(x,y)$$

*These functions are obviously constant on the equivalence relation (see Chapter A) on* $X \times M(X,Z)$ *whose quotient space is* $M^2(X,Z)$. *Denote the corresponding functions on* $M^2(X,Z)$ *as:*

$$p,q,r,s,t \quad .$$

*Thus, in a sense, these letters are identified with the following linear differential operators:*

$$p = \frac{\partial}{\partial x}$$

$$q = \frac{\partial}{\partial y}$$

$$r = \frac{\partial^2}{\partial x^2}$$

$$s = \frac{\partial^2}{\partial x \partial y}$$

$$t = \frac{\partial^2}{\partial y^2} \quad .$$

A _coordinate system_ for $M^2(X,Z)$ _is then provided by the functions_

$$(x,y,z,p,q,r,s,t)$$

_Now, consider the space of maps_

$$R^7 \to M^2(X,Z)$$

_following from:_

$$(x,y,z,p,q,r,t) \to (x,y,z,p,q,r\text{-}F(x,y,z,p,q,s,t),t)$$

_(In other words, we identify_ $M^2(X,Z)$ _with_

$$R^r \times R$$

_and consider the maps_

$$R^r \to M^2(X,Z)$$

_which are_ _graphs_ _of mappings_

$$R^r \to R \quad .)$$

*Let* G = *group of diffeomorphisms of* X × Z *(≡ space of variables* (x,y,z)*). Extend* G *by prolongation to act on* $M^2(X,Z)$.

*Now, extend* G *to act on the contact element manifolds:*

$$C^j(M^2(X,Z),r)$$

*for* j = 0,1,2,...

*This action is essentially the "action of the group of point transformations on 2-nd order partial differential equations".*

*Another possibility for* G *which was extensively considered by Lie and his comtemporaries (e.g., Darboux, Goursat) is the group of* <u>contact transformations</u>. *This is the group of diffeomorphisms of* (x,y,z,p,q) *space (which is, invariantly,* $M^1(X,Z)$ *) which preserves* <u>up to a factor</u> *the one-form*

$$dz - pdx - qdy \quad .$$

## 4.12   INVARIANT THEORY OF SOME SPECIAL SECOND ORDER PARTIAL DIFFERENTIAL EQUATIONS

The invariant theory of <u>algebraic</u> partial differential equations is simpler. Consider, in particular, an equation of the form

$$r + Bs + Ct + D = 0 \quad .$$

Introduce new variables

$$x_1 = X(x,y,z), \qquad y_1 = Y, \qquad z_1 = Z \qquad (4.12.1)$$

to get an equation of the analogous form

$$r_1 + B_1 s_1 + C_1 t_1 + D_1 = 0 \quad ,$$

where $p_1, q_1, B_1, C_1, D_1$ are functions of $p, q, B, C, D$ and of $X, Y, Z$ and their derivatives

$$p_1 = P \;,\ldots,\; D_1 = F \qquad (4.12.2)$$

The equations (4.12.1), (4.12.2) obviously determine an infinite group, whose infinitesimal transformations are found by computing $\delta p$, $\delta q$, $\delta r$, $\delta s$, $\delta t$ and introducing the computed values into the equation

$$\delta r + B\delta s + C\delta t + s\delta B + t\delta C + \delta D = 0 \quad .$$

Thus one sees the existence of invariants of the form

$$\Omega(p, q, B, C, D, B_x, B_y, \ldots) \quad .$$

On the other hand, consider the <u>Monge-Ampère</u> equation

$$rt - s^2 + Ar + Bs + Ct + D = 0 \quad .$$

Applying an arbitrary contact-transformation takes this into a new equation of the analogous form

$$r_1 t_1 - s_1^2 + A_1 r_1 + B_1 s_1 + C_1 t_1 + D_1 = 0 \quad ,$$

where $A_1, B_1, C_1, D_1$ are functions of $A, B, C, D$. We again
get an infinite group, which yields invariants of the form

$$\Omega(x, y, z, p, q, A, B, C, D, A_x, A_y, \ldots) \quad .$$

## 4.13    INVARIANT THEORY OF LINEAR ORDINARY DIFFERENTIAL
EQUATIONS

As is well-known, the extremely important problem of
finding all invariants of the linear equation

$$y^{(r)} + X_{r-1} y^{(r-1)} + \cdots + X_1 y' + Xy = 0 \quad (4.13.1)$$

with respect to the infinite group

$$x_1 = \Phi(x), \qquad y_1 = yF(x)$$

has been treated by Laguerre and, more thoroughly, by
Halphen. At the same time one can pose the more general
question of the covariants. Laguerre and Halphen have
developed an integration theory for those linear equations
(4.13.1) which can be transformed into a linear equation
with constant coefficients. Essentially, this theory is
subsumed as a special case of the integration theory of
equations

$$f(x, y, y', \ldots, y^{(m)}) = 0$$

with a continuous group, which I announced in 1874 and
carried out in detail in 1882-83 (Gött. Nachr., Dec. 1874;

Archiv for Math. og Nat. Vols. VII and VIII, 1882-83
[Collected Papers Vol. V, papers I, IX, X, XI, XIV].)

I emphasize that Halphen's beautiful investigations
of linear differential equations (Mémoire sur la réduction
des équations différentielles linéaires aux formes inté-
grables, prize work, presented 1880, published 1883) extend
immediately to those equations

$$f(x,y,y',y'',\ldots,y^{(m)}) = 0$$

which are reducible to integrable linear equations by some
(unspecified) point- or contact-transformation (Ges. d.
Wiss. zu Chr. 1883: Untersuchungen über Differentialgleichungen III (Investigations of differential equations III)
[Collected Papers Vol. V, paper XII, pp. 311-313]). I shall
return to this.


4.14   LINEAR SECOND ORDER PARTIAL DIFFERENTIAL EQUATIONS

A linear (second-order) partial differential equation

$$r + Ss + Tt + Pp + Qq + Zz = 0 \qquad (4.14.1)$$

whose coefficients $S,T,\ldots,Z$ depend only on $x$ and $y$,
assumes the linear form

$$r_1 + S_1 s_1 + T_1 t_1 + P_p p_1 + Q_1 q_1 + Z_1 z_1 = 0$$

under an arbitrary transformation of the infinite group

$$z_1 = z \cdot F(x,y), \qquad x_1 = X(x,y), \qquad y_1 = Y(x,y) \quad (4.14.2)$$

The equations which define the new coefficients in terms of
the old, when taken together with (4.14.2), form an infinite
group. One first computes the increments $\delta S, \delta T, \ldots, \delta Z$
produced by an infinitesimal transformation of the latter
group and then finds arbitrarily many invariants (and covariants) of the equation (4.14.1) with respect to our group.


## 4.15    CURVATURE AS A DIFFERENTIAL INVARIANT

By the procedure of <u>Gauss</u> we bring the element of
arc-length of an arbitrary surface into the form

$$ds^2 = Edx^2 + 2Fdxdy + Gdy^2 \quad . \qquad (4.15.1)$$

By introducing new variables

$$x_1 = X(x,t), \qquad y_1 = Y(x,y)$$

the arc-length element assumes the new form

$$ds^2 = E_1 dx_1^2 + 2F_1 dx_1 dy_1 + G_1 dy_1^2 \quad .$$

In this, $E_1, F_1, G_1$ are determined as functions of $E, F, G$,
$x, y$ by certain relations which, taken together with
$x_1 = X$, $y_1 = Y$ form an infinite group. To find the invariants (and covariants) of this group discovered by <u>Gauss</u> and

his successors by means of general rules, we first vary the
equation (4.15.1), considering  ds  to be constant:

$$\delta E \cdot dx^2 + 2\delta F \cdot dxdy + \delta G \cdot dy^2 + \{2(Edx+Fdy)d\xi+2(Fdx+Gdy)d\eta\}\delta t = 0$$

to obtain the relations

$$\frac{-\delta E}{\delta t} = 2E\xi_x + 2F\eta_x \quad,$$

$$\frac{-\delta F}{\delta t} = E\xi y + F\xi_x + F\eta_y + G\eta_x \quad,$$

$$\frac{-\delta G}{\delta t} = 2F\xi_y + 2G\eta_y \quad.$$

We then form the equations

$$\delta(dE-E_x dx - E_y dy) = 0,\ldots$$

and thus find the increments of  $E_x, E_y, \ldots, G_y$.  Continuing
in the familiar way, it is evident that we first find the
Gaussian curvature.

    If we adjoin to the group just considered the equa-
tions which determine  $y_1', y_1'', \ldots$  as functions of
$x, y, y', y'', \ldots,$  we get invariants containing the derivatives
of  y.

    Instead of  $y', y'', \ldots$  one can introduce a function
$\Phi$  of  x,y  (or several such).  In the variables  $x_1, y_1,$
$\Phi$  has the new form

$$\Phi_1(x_1, y_1) = \Phi(x,y) \quad,$$

while its <u>value</u> is unchanged. Hence we put $\delta\Phi = 0$ and
likewise

$$\delta(d\Phi - \Phi_x dx - \Phi_y dy) = 0 ,$$

whence

$$-\frac{\delta\Phi_x}{\delta t} = \Phi_x \xi_x + \Phi_y \eta_x ,$$

$$-\frac{\delta\Phi_y}{\delta t} = \Phi_x \xi_y + \Phi_y \eta_y .$$

Substituting these, and the values of $\delta E, \delta F, \delta G$ determined
before into

$$B' = X\frac{\partial}{\partial x} + Y\frac{\partial}{\partial y} + \frac{\delta E}{\delta t}\frac{\partial}{\partial E} + \cdots + \frac{\delta\Phi_x}{\delta t}\frac{\partial}{\partial\Phi_x} + \frac{\delta\Phi_y}{\delta t}\frac{\partial}{\partial\Phi_y} ,$$

we obtain the infinitesimal transformations of a group.
All the equations of the form $B'f = 0$ have a common solution, namely, the invariant introduced by <u>Beltrami</u>

$$\frac{E\Phi_y^2 - 2F\Phi_x\Phi_y + G\Phi_x^2}{EG - F^2} ,$$

and so forth.

The preceding considerations can be significantly
simplified by the hypothesis

$$E = G = 0, \qquad \xi_y = \eta_x = 0 .$$

*COMMENTS*

 *Here is one interpretation of this material.  Let
X be a two-dimensional manifold.  A <u>Riemannian metric</u> β
in X is an F(X)-bilinear, symmetric form*

$$\beta: V(X) \times V(X) \to F(X) \quad,$$

*which is also <u>non-degenerate</u>.*

 *Let*

$$RIE(X)$$

*be the space of Riemannian metrics.  There is a fiber space*

$$E \to X$$

*(whose fiber above a point x ∈ X is the space of twice
covariant, non-degenerate tensors), whose space of cross-
sections is identified with RIE(X), i.e.,*

$$RIE(X) = \Gamma(E)$$

*Let*

$$G = \text{group of diffeomorphisms of } X.$$

*Let G act in RIE(X) as follows:*

$$g(\beta)(A_1,A_2) = g^{-1}*(\beta(g_*^{-1}(A_1),g_*^{-1}(A_2)))$$
$$\text{for } g \in G; \quad A_1,A_2 \in V(X); \quad \beta \in RM(X)$$

*Then*

$$g(\beta) = \beta$$

*means that g is an <u>isometry</u> of the metric β.*

 *Now, G acting in this way on RIE(X) ≡ Γ(E) arises
from an action of G via fiber space automorphisms on Γ(E):*

$$g(\beta)(x) = g(\beta g^{-1}(x))$$

*for* $g \in G$, $\beta \in \Gamma(E)$, $x \in X$ .

*Remark*. G, *acting on* E, *is the "natural" action of diffeomorphisms on tensors.*

*We can then form*

$$J^r(E)$$

*the* r-*jets of cross-sections of* E. *It may be defined in the following way.*

*First, given* $A \in V(X)$, $\beta \in RIE(X)$, *let*

$$A(\beta)$$

*be the* Lie derivative of $\beta$. *It is a symmetric,* F(X)-*bilinear map*

$$V(X) \times V(X) \to F(X)$$

*defined by the following formula:*

$$A(\beta)(A_1,A_2) = A(\beta(A_1,A_2)) - \beta([A,A_1],A_2) - \beta(A_1,[A,A_2])$$

*One can then iterate the Lie derivative construction, forming*

$$A_1(A_2(\beta)) \quad ,$$

*and so forth.*

_Definition_.  $\beta_1, \beta_2 \in \text{RIE}(X)$  _agree to the_ **r**-_th order_ at
$x \in X$  _if the following conditions are satisfied:_

$$\beta_1(x) \;=\; \beta_2(x)$$
$$A_1(\beta_1)(x) \;=\; A_1(\beta_2)(x)$$
$$\vdots$$
$$A_1(\ldots A_r(\beta_1))(x) \;=\; A_1(\ldots A_r(\beta_2))(x)$$

_for all_  $A_1, \ldots, A_r \in V(X)$

_Definition_.  $J^r(E)$  _is the quotient of_

$$X \times \text{RIE}(X)$$

_by the following equivalence relation:_

$(x_1, \beta_1)$  _is equivalent to_  $(x_2, \beta_2)$  _if:_
$x_1 = x_2$;  $\beta_1$  _and_  $\beta_2$  _agree to order_ r _at_ $x_1$.

$G$  $(\equiv \text{DIFF}(X))$  _also acts in a natural way on_  $J^r(E)$  _as fiber
space automorphisms._  _An_ r-_th order differential invariant_
_of_  $G$  _is a mapping_

$$\Omega: J^r(E) \rightarrow R$$

_which is_ _invariant_ _under the action of_  $G$  _on_  $J^r(E)$.

        _So far, these definitions are very general._  $X$  _could
be any sort of manifold, and_  $E$  _could be any subbundle
of a bundle of tensors associated with the manifold structure of_  E.  _Now we use the hypothesis_

dim X = 2,   β = *Riemannian metric*

*in the following way.  The* <u>*Gaussian curvature*</u> *is a mapping*

$$\beta \rightarrow K(\beta)$$

*of* : RIE(X) → F(X)

*We shall see that it defines a* <u>*second order differential*</u>
<u>*invariant*</u>.

*One can do this in the classical way, as indicated*
*obliquely by Lie.  Let  (x,y)  be coordinates on  X.  Any*
*β ε* RIE(X)  *can be written in the classical notation:*

$$\beta \equiv ds^3 = Edx^2 + 2Fdxdy + Gdy^2$$

*Set:*

$$H^2 = EG - 4F^2 \equiv \textit{discriminant of the}$$
$$\textit{quadratic form } \beta.$$

*Define*  K(β)  *as:*

$$2HK(\beta) = \frac{\partial}{\partial x}\left( \frac{F}{EH}\frac{\partial E}{\partial y} - \frac{1}{H}\frac{\partial G}{\partial x} \right)$$

$$+ \frac{\partial}{\partial y}\left( \frac{2}{H}\frac{\partial F}{\partial x} - \frac{1}{H}\frac{\partial E}{\partial y} - \frac{F}{EH}\frac{\partial E}{\partial x} \right)$$

*Gauss' Main Theorem is that*

$$\beta \rightarrow K(\beta)$$

*satisfies the following covariance condition:*

$$g^*(K(\beta)) \;=\; K(g^{-1}(\beta))$$

$$\textit{for all} \quad \beta \;\epsilon\; \text{RIE}(X) \quad .$$

*Notice from this formula that* K *depends on the derivatives up to the* <u>*second order*</u> *of the* E, F, G.

  *Let us follow Cartan's* <u>*method of the moving frame*</u> *for deducing this property. Let* $\omega_1, \omega_2$ *be one-forms on* X *such that*

$$\beta \;\equiv\; ds^2 \;=\; \omega_1^2 + \omega_2^2$$

<u>*Remark*</u>. *We are thus restricting attention, for simplicity, to positive metrics. Everything carries over to the general case. Let* $\omega_{12}, \omega_{21}$ *be one-forms with the following properties:*

$$\omega_{12} \;=\; {}^-\omega_{21}$$

$$d\omega_1 \;=\; \omega_{12} \wedge \omega_2$$

$$d\omega_2 \;=\; \omega_{21} \wedge \omega_1$$

$\omega_{12}$ *is then uniquely defined by* $(\omega_1, \omega_2)$ *and these conditions. It is called the* <u>*connection form*</u>. K($\beta$) *is then characterized by the following property:*

$$d\omega_{12} \;=\; k(\beta)\omega_1 \wedge \omega_2 \quad .$$

  *If* g *is a diffeomorphism of* X, *then:*

$$g(\beta) \;=\; (g^{-1})^*(\omega_1)^2 + (g^{-1})^*(\omega_2)^2$$

*Hence, the connection form of the metric* $g(\beta)$ *is:*

$$(g^{-1})^*(\omega_{12}) \quad .$$

*Thus,*

$$d((g^{-1})^*(\omega_{12})) \quad = \quad K(g(\beta))(g^{-1}*(\omega_1 \wedge \omega_2)$$

*also,*

$$d((g^{-1})^*(\omega_{12})) \quad = \quad g^{-1}*(d\omega_{12})$$

$$= \quad g^{-1}*(K(\beta)\omega_1 \wedge \omega_2)$$

*Equating these two expressions gives:*

$$g^{-1}*(K(\beta)) \quad = \quad K(g(\beta)) \quad ,$$

*or*

$$g*(K(\beta)) \quad = \quad K(g^{-1}(\beta)) \quad ,$$

*which is the covariance property.*

*Now, let us prove that this property implies Lie's* <u>*differential invariant*</u> *property.*

*Define a function*

$$\overline{\Omega}: X \times RIE(X) \to R$$

*by the following formula:*

$$\overline{\Omega}(x,\beta) \quad = \quad K(\beta)(x)$$

*We see (e.g., from the classical explicit formula for the Gaussian curvature given above) that* $\overline{\Omega}$ *is constant on the equivalence relation (for* $r=2$ *) and passes to the quotient to define the function*

$$\Omega: J^2(E) \to R \quad .$$

*Explicitly,*

$$\Omega(\partial^2(\beta)(x)) \;=\; K(\beta)(x) \quad .$$

  *Let us show that* $\Omega$ *is invariant under the action of* G.

$$
\begin{aligned}
\Omega(g(\partial^2(\beta)(x)) \;&=\; \Omega(\partial^2(g(\beta))(gx))) \\[2mm]
&=\; K(g(\beta))(gx) \\[2mm]
&=\; g^*(K(g\beta))(x) \\[2mm]
&=\; K(g^{-1}g\beta)(x) \\[2mm]
&=\; K(\beta)(x) \;=\; \Omega(\partial^2(\beta)(x)) \quad .
\end{aligned}
$$

*Hence,*

$$\Omega(g\gamma) \;=\; \Omega(\gamma)$$

$$\text{for all } \gamma \in J^3(E) \quad .$$

  *Ricci and Levi-Civita, in their 1900 Tensor Analysis paper develop the interrelation between Lie's "differential invariant" viewpoint and the now traditional differential geometric framework for Riemannian Geometry. They show that the covariant derivatives of the Gaussian curvature determines differential invariants of order 3,4,..., and that these form a basis for differential invariants, in the sense that an arbitrary differential invariant can be written as a function of these. In fact, there are certain interesting global questions inherent, but not explicitly considered, in this classical approach that I mean to write on later, using methods developed in my paper   "Homo-morphisms of absolute parallelism".*

*Of course, it is, in this case, much simpler to use a special geometric technique (in this case, the existence of the Riemannian connection) to construct these differen-tial invariants than to use directly Lie's general method. This seems to be quite typical: Lie's method is cumbersome in interesting geometric circumstances, and the "differen-tial invariants" must be computed by differential-geometric tools which are more suited to studying the detailed geome-tric properties of the special situation. Judging from the tone of his paper, Lie apparently was rather irritated when his contemporaries developed special techniques rather than using his general theory.*

*The two most serious attempts to develop Lie's general method seem to have been in a paper by   Tresse [1] in 1894 (apparently, he was Lie's student) and Cartan's method of the "répère mobile". Unfortunately, neither is a master-piece of lucidity, although no doubt both methods could be pushed much further now with our vastly improved notation, and knowledge of differential topology, Lie groups  and Lie algebra theory, etc. It is an amazing commentary on the*

*perversity of mathematical taste that this extremely impor-*
*tant topic has, with the exception of Cartan, been hardly*
*worked on, at least by the "mainstream" of mathematicians*
*since Lie's death.  In Chapter B I will develop further*
*material that I hope will contribute to the revival of*
*interest, and more important, to the application of the*
*ideas, both inside and outside of mathematics.*

## 4.16    INVARIANT THEORY OF FIRST ORDER PARTIAL DIFFERENTIAL EQUATIONS

As I indicated in Göttingen Nachr. 1872, p. 479
[Collected Papers Vol. III, paper IV, p. 19f.], one can
determine the invariants of a first-order partial differential equation in the variables $z, x_1, \ldots, x_n$ under the
group of all point-transformations.  Then one might look
for the synthetic interpretation of the simplest of these
invariants.  For example, one might try to set up the
invariant relations which must hold if our equation has a
complete integral defined by several relations among
$z, x_1, \ldots, x_n$.  I have not yet found time to more closely
discuss these questions, which I considered in an incident-
al way in 1872.

4.17    CONTINUATION

In   r   given functions   $F_1, F_2, \ldots, F_r$   of   $x_1, \ldots, x_n$,
$p_1, \ldots, p_n$   introduce new variables   $x_k'$, $p_i'$   by means of an
arbitrary contact-transformation for which there is a rela-
tion of the form

$$p_i' \; dx_i' \; = \; p_i \; dx_i + dV \; .$$

Each   $F_k$   assumes a new form   $F_k'$   in the new variables,
while its value is unchanged.  Recall now that any infinitesimal contact-transformation has the symbol   $(W,f)$,
where   $W$   is an arbitrary function of   $x_k, p_k$,   and where
( , )   denotes Poisson bracket;   then one can easily set
up the defining equations of all differential invariants
of the   $F_k$   with respect to the group of all contact-
transformations.  It is easy to verify the well-known
theorem that all the expressions   $(F_i, F_k)$, $((F_i, F_k), F_j), \ldots$
are invariants, and one sees that all invariants can be
expressed by iteration of the Poisson-Jacobi operation
(cf. Math. Ann. Vol. VIII, pp. 270-273, 297-298 [Collected
Papers Vol. IX, paper I, §16 and §24, No. 51]).[*]

In the work just cited I settled the question of
whether   r   given functions   $F_1, \ldots, F_r$   of   $x_1, \ldots, p_n$   can

_____
[*] Note that when   r   is sufficiently large, the $\frac{1}{2}$ r(r-1)
quantities   $(F_i F_k)$   are connected by certain finite relations
which are independent of the form of the functions   $F_k$.

be transformed into  r  given functions  $F_1', \ldots, F_r'$  of
$x_1', \ldots, p_n'$  by a contact-transformation.  This problem can
be reduced to the case where the  $F_k$  are independent and
there are relations of the form

$$(F_i, F_k) \;=\; \Omega_{ik}(F_1, F_2, \ldots, F_r) \quad .$$

Then such a transformation exists if and only if the  $F_k'$
are independent and satisfy the analogous relations

$$(F_i', F_k') \;=\; \Omega_{ik}(F_1', \ldots, F_r') \quad .$$

Since the  $F_k$  are invariants of a contact-
transformation (i.e.,  $F_k = F_k'$) the preceding criterion
amounts to the condition that certain relations among the
invariants which hold in the original variables continue
to hold in the new variables.

Chapter 5

CONCLUDING REMARKS

## 5.1 THE EQUIVALENCE PROBLEM

In answer to the question of whether certain differential equations $F_k = 0$ or analytic expressions $\Phi_k$ can
be brought into a given form by a transformation of a given
continuous group, one easily obtains a necessary condition
in the form of invariant differential relations.

For example, a differential form $X\,dx + Y\,dy$ is
exact if and only if $X_y - Y_x = 0$, as is well-known. The
form of this conditional equation is unchanged by all point-
transformations.

Similarly, the theory of the Pfaffian problem gives
a series of criteria which have an invariant character with
respect to all point-transformations.

To decide whether a surface with element of arc-length

$$ds^2 = Edx^2 + 2Fdxdy + Gdy^2$$

can be transformed onto another surface with element of
arc-length

$$ds_1^2 = E_1 dx_1^2 + 2F_1 dx_1 dy_1 + G_1 dy_1^2 \ ,$$

according to the rules of <u>Minding</u> one computes certain
differential invariants $A, B, C$ for both surfaces as functions

141

of  x  and  y,  and then determines the relations among
A,B,C by eliminating  x  and  y.  If one finds only one
such relation, say

$$A = \Omega(B,C)$$

then its form is a true picture of all the properties of
the surface which are invariant under bending.  Two surfaces
can be bent onto each other if their  A,B,C  are connected
by the same relation.  A,B,C  are connected by several relations if the surface can be displaced into itself without
stretching.

According to my old investigations,  m  given func-
tions  $F_1, F_2, \ldots, F_m$  of  $x_1, \ldots, x_n$, $p_1, \ldots, p_n$  can be
transformed into  $x'_1, x'_2, \ldots, x'_m$  or  $p'_1, \ldots, p'_m$  by a contact-
transformation if and only if the  $\frac{1}{2}m(m-1)$  expressions
$(F_i, F_k)$  vanish identically.  Each  $(F_i, F_k)$  is an invariant
of all contact transformations.

According to my investigations cited earlier, to
decide whether given functions  $F_1, F_2, \ldots, F_r$  of  $x_1, \ldots, x_n$
$p_1, \ldots, p_n$  can be transformed into given functions  $F'_1, \ldots, F'_r$
of  $x'_1, \ldots, p'_n$  by a contact-transformation, one forms a
certain number of the invariants  $(F_i, F_k), \ldots$  and determines the relations among them.  The transformation is
possible if and only if the two cases give the same relations.

If $F_1, \ldots, F_r$ and $\rho+1$ <u>arbitrary</u> differential invariants of them are connected by a relation, then each $F_k$ admits $2n-r-\rho$ essentially distinct infinitesimal transformations. Indeed, under these hypotheses the $F_k$ determine a group whose polar group contains $2n-r-\rho$ independent functions.[*]

To determine whether a given function

$$F(x,y,p,q,r,s,t)$$

can be transformed to a given function

$$F'(x',y',z',p',q',r',s',t')$$

by a contact-transformation, one determines the differential invariants $J_1, J_2, \ldots$ of $F$ under the group of contact-transformations and computes them as functions of $x,y,z,\ldots,t$:

$$J_k = J_k(x,y,\ldots,s,t) \quad .$$

Thus one obtains arbitrarily many relations

$$J_k(x,\ldots,t) = J_k'(x',\ldots,t') \quad .$$

If none of these equations is contradictory, then the transformation is possible.

---

[*] See Math. Ann. Vol. VIII, Begründung einer Invarianten-theorie der Berührungstransformationen (Foundations of an invariant theory of contact transformations), p. 217 and 270 [Collected Papers Vol. IV, paper I, Einl. (Introduction) and §16].

If  F  admits one or several infinitesimal contact-transformations into itself, then any eight of the  $J_k$  are connected by a relation, and so on.

It is especially easy to answer the question (as I was the first to do) of whether a given equation

$$f(x,y,\ldots,r,s,t) = 0$$

can be reduced to the form  $s = 0$  or  $r = 0$.

*COMMENTS ON CHAPTER 5*

*Here Lie briefly (but masterfully) describes one of the most general but also most interesting geometric problems and ideas to come out of his work--to develop criteria that two geometric structures be "equivalent" (or transformable into each other) under the action of a given transformation group.  Cartan put this problem at the forefront of his theory of infinite Lie groups and differential geometry, and developed many more general ideas and applications of the geometric ideas to specific and interesting examples.  Even this remains in an incomplete state today, and much more work needs to be done.*

*A basic idea in Cartan's equivalence theory is that geometric structures may be put into a certain standard form, parameterized by subgroups  G  of the group of  $n \times n$*

*real matrices.  For this reason, they are called* G-*structures
in the recent geometric literature, although that is a bar-
baric name which signifies nothing to someone outside the
field.  (I suggest the name* <u>Cartan structures, with structure
group</u>  G.)*

*If*  X  *is a manifold dimension*  n,  *and*  G  *is a subgroup of*  GL(n,R),  *the group of* n×n *real matrices, then
such a Cartan structure is defined by a* <u>reduction</u> *of the
structure group of the principle tangent frame bundle from*
GL(n,R)  *to*  G.  *(Steenrod* [1] *is the standard reference for
fiber bundle theory.)  Equivalently, such a reduction may
be defined by a* <u>cross-section</u> *of a fiber space over*  X,
*whose fiber is the coset space*

GL(n,R)/G  .

*Cartan's theory is developed throughout Parts II and
III of his Collected Works.  The most fundamental and/or
systematic papers are 26, 30 and 161 in Part II.*

*The four examples of equivalence problems given in
this chapter were much more extensively treated by Cartan
in a more general context.  The first is the equivalence of
differential forms and exterior differential systems.  See
papers 14, 15, 19, 30, 40, 42, and 44 in Part II of Cartan's
Oeuvres.*

*The second example is equivalence of Riemannian metrics. Now, a "Riemannian metric" is a Cartan structure with O(n,R), the orthogonal group, as structure group. It is one of those that are of "finite type", in the sense that a bundle can be constructed over X (in this case, the principal orthonormal frame bundle) and an* <u>*absolute parallelism*</u> *(i.e., a basis for one-forms) can be constructed on this bundle which decides the equivalence problem, i.e., two such Cartan structures are equivalent if and only if the absolute parallelisms are equivalent. See my paper [1] "Cartan connections and the equivalence problem for geometric structures". An extremely interesting qualitative feature is that the existence of this parallelism can be shown to depend only on an algebraic property of the matrix group G.*

*The third example--equivalence of sets of functions under canonical transformations--is very important for the calculus of variations, control theory, classical and quantum mechanics. Cartan provided a definitive treatment in paper 14 of Part II of his collected Works. This is material that is periodically reproved again and again (usually in an incomplete or incompetent form) in the mathematics and physics literature--most recently in connection with the theory of what mathematicians now call the theory*

of *Lagrangian submanifolds of symplectic manifolds*. Physicists working on the quantization of classical mechanical
systems are also blissfully ignorant of Lie's work. If Lie
were still alive, no doubt he would be expressing his
irritation that people do not use his general theory!

The final example--the equivalence of second order
partial differential equations--is virtually untouched
since Lie's day. There is a much further development in
Goursat's book "Lecons sur l'intégration des équations
aux derivés partielles du second ordre" and in Cartan's
paper No. 30 in Part II of the Oeuvres. (This is the
notorious "Five Variables" paper, one of the most difficult,
and probably one of the most profound, in all mathematics.
One reason for its difficulty is that the reader has to be
familiar with the whole literature of the 19-th century
theory of partial differential equations.) I believe that
it would be very important for applications--e.g., quantum
field theory and continuum mechanics--to revive this work,
understand its modern significance, and extend it to  other
systems of partial differential equations!


Christiania,   29 May 1884.

Chapter B

FURTHER WORK IN THE THEORY OF
DIFFERENTIAL INVARIANTS


1.    DIFFERENTIAL INVARIANTS AND DIFFERENTIAL OPERATORS

We have seen that Lie's ideas provide a precise
foundation for the notion of "differential invariant".  Now,
these objects often arise more naturally as "differential
operators".  It will then be useful to develop the relation
between the two concepts.

In VB and GPS I developed material concerning linear
differential operators.  The ideas needed in this volume
essentially involve generalizations to non-linear differential
operators.  Although I do not yet see this theory in as
complete an algebraic form, it is worthwhile describing some
general ideas.

Let  X, Z  and  W  be manifolds.  Recall that, for
each integer  r,

$$M^r(X,Z)$$

denotes the space of mapping elements of maps  $\phi: X \to Z$.
$M(X,Z)$  denotes the space of these maps.

$$\partial^r \phi: X \to M^r(X,Z)$$

denotes the prolongation of the map  $\phi$.

<u>Definition</u>.  A map

$$\Delta: M(X,Z) \to M(X,W)$$

is an r-th order <u>differential operator</u> if there is a map

$$\delta: M^r(X,Z) \to W$$

such that:

$$\Delta(\phi)(x) = \delta(\partial^r \phi(x)) \qquad (1.1)$$

for all  $x \in X$,  all  $\phi \in M(X,Z)$  .

In mapping diagram terms, the following diagram of mappings
is <u>commutative</u>:

$$(1.2)$$

<u>Definition</u>.  Let  $\Delta: M(X,Z) \to M(X,W)$  be an r-th order differ-
ential operator defined by a map  $\delta: M^r(X,Z) \to W$.  Consider

$$M^r(X,Z) \to M^{r-1}(X,Z) \qquad (1.3)$$

as a fiber space.  (The map (1.3) is the result of "forgetting"
the r-th order derivatives, i.e., if two maps  $\phi, \phi_1: X \to Z$
agree to the order r at a point  x,  they also agree to order
(r-1).  Then,  $\delta$,  restricted to the fibers of the map (1.3),
is called the <u>symbol</u> of  $\Delta$.

Here is the main result of this section:

Theorem 1.1. Let $G$ be a group of diffeomorphisms of $X$, $Z$ and $W$. Let $G$ act on $M(X,Z)$ as follows:

$$g(\phi)(x) = g(\phi(g^{-1}x))$$

$$\text{for } x \in X, \quad \phi \in M(X,Z) \quad .$$

Similarly, let $G$ act on $M(X,W)$ and $M^r(X,Z)$. Let $\Delta: M(X,Z) \to M(X,W)$ be a differential operator defined by a map

$$\delta: M^r(X,Z) \to W \quad .$$

Then, $\Delta$ intertwines the action of $G$ on $M(X,Z)$ and $M(X,W)$ if and only if $\delta$ intertwines the action of $G$ on $M^r(X,Z)$ and $W$.

Proof. Suppose first that $\Delta$ intertwines $G$. Then, for $\phi \in M(X,Z)$, $x \in X$, $g \in G$,

$$\delta(g((\partial^r\phi)(x)) = \delta(\partial^r(g(\phi))(gx))$$

$$= \Delta(g\phi)(gx)$$

$$= g(\Delta\phi)(gx)$$

$$= g(\Delta\phi(g^{-1}gx))$$

$$= g(\Delta\phi(x))$$

$$= g(\delta(\partial^r\phi(x)))$$

This shows that $\delta$ intertwines G. The steps are reversible to prove the converse.

Example. Riemannian geometry provides many examples of non-linear differential operators. If $\beta$: $V(X) \times V(X) \rightarrow F(X)$ defines a Riemannian metrix, $\beta$ defines a dual map

$$\beta^d: F^1(X) \times F^1(X) \rightarrow F(X)$$

on one-forms. (In Volume V of IM this is called a contra-variant Riemannian metric.) The mapping

$$f \rightarrow \beta^d(df,df) \equiv \Delta_1(f)$$

of $M(X,R) \rightarrow M(X,R)$ is called the first Beltrami operator. It intertwines the groups of isometries of the metric $\beta$.

It can, more broadly, be considered as a map

$$RIE (X) \times M(X,R) \rightarrow M(X,R)$$

In this form, it intertwines the action of the group of diffe-omorphisms of X. (This fact is emphasized in Ricci and Levi-Civita's approach to Riemannian geometry--see my translation of their 1900 paper.) Similarly, the Riemannian curvature tensor is a second order non-linear differential operator

$$RIE (X) \rightarrow (cross-section of a vector bundle on  X)$$

which is invariant under the group of diffeomorphisms of X. The invariance of this mapping (and the contracted Ricci curvature tensor mapping) plays the key role in what Einstein called the "General Covariance of Gravitational Field."

One encounters many examples of non-linear differential operators in the calculus of variations. A Lagrangian is such an object. The Euler-Lagrange operator is another.


2.      ALGEBRAIC AND DIFFERENTIAL INVARIANTS OF THE ONE-
        VARIABLE PROJECTIVE GROUP

Virtually every branch of geometry, physics and engineering can provide examples and situations where Lie's ideas apply in one form or another. The branch called "projective differential geometry" seems to be the area which historically has been in closest contact.

In the next few sections I will describe certain aspects of this field in the light of Lie's ideas. For background, see Cartan [2] and Wilczynsky [1]. We begin with the simplest situation--the action of the $G \equiv GL(2,R)$ (as linear fractional transformations) on T, the real numbers.

If

$$g = \begin{pmatrix} a,b \\ c,d \end{pmatrix} \in GL(2,R) \equiv G$$

$$x \in R ,$$

then:

$$gx = \frac{ax + b}{cx + d} . \qquad\qquad (2.1)$$

Let  G' ⊂ G  be the invariant subgroup of  G  consisting of the  2×2  real matrices of determinant one . This group
is usually denoted by

　　　SL(2,R)

G'  also acts transitively on  R.  Here is the precise situation.

Let  C  be the subgroup of  G  consisting of the  2×2
diagonal matrices with equal diagonal elements.  C  is the
center of  G.  C  acts trivially on  R,  hence

　　　G/C

is the group which acts effectively on  R(≡PS(R$^2$)).  This
group is often denoted by

　　　PGL(2,R)

　　　G'∩ C

is the group with two elements, namely

$$\begin{pmatrix} 1 & 0 \\ 0 & 1 \end{pmatrix} \quad \text{and} \quad \begin{pmatrix} -1 & 0 \\ 0 & -1 \end{pmatrix}$$

(This group with two elements is denoted by  C$_2$,  called the
cyclic group of period two.)

Hence,

　　　G' ∩ C  =  C$_2$  .

However,

$$G = G'C .$$

Thus, G is not the direct product of G' and C at the Lie group level, i.e., the group extension

$$G \to G/C$$

does not "split". (Since the intersection $G' \cap C$ is discrete, it does split at the Lie algebra level, which is often all one needs to know.) G' does act transitively on R, so most questions about the action of G on R can be reduced to the action of G' on R.

The first step is to study the zero-th order differential invariants, i.e.,,the "invariants in the sense of algebra".

Theorem 2.1.  Suppose that

$$(x_1, x_2, x_3), \ (x_1', x_2', x_3')$$

are two triples of distinct real numbers.  Then, there is a g ε G such that

$$(gx_1, gx_2, gx_3) = (x_1', x_2', x_3')$$

In particular, there is no function

$$f: R \times R \times R \to R ,$$

which is invariant under the action of G, i.e., such that:

$$f(gx_1, gx_2, gx_3) = f(x_1, x_2, x_3)$$
$$\text{for } x_1, x_2, x_3 \ \varepsilon \ R, \quad \text{all } g \ \varepsilon \ G' .$$

Proof. Let $V$ be the vector space $R^2$, consisting of the pairs

$$v = (y_1, y_2)$$

of real numbers. Let $V'$ be the set of points of $V$ such that

$$y_2 \neq 0 .$$

Define a map

$$\pi: V' \to R$$

as follows:

$$\pi(y_1, y_2) = \frac{y_1}{y_2} .$$

(In the classical language, $(y_1, y_2)$ are called homogeneous coordinates for $R$.)

Let $G \equiv GL(2, R) \equiv GL(V)$ act in its natural way on $V$. $\pi$ intertwines the action of $G$ on $V$ and $R$.

Given

$$(x_1, x_2, x_3), \; (x_1', x_2', x_3') \; \varepsilon \; R \times R \times R ,$$

choose

$$(v_1, v_2, v_3), \; (v_1', v_2', v_3') \; \varepsilon \; V' \times V' \times V'$$

such that

$$\pi(v_1) = x_1 , \qquad \pi(v_1') = x_1'$$

$$\pi(v_2) = x_2 , \qquad \pi(v_2') = x_2'$$

$$\pi(v_3) = x_3 , \qquad \pi(v_3') = x_3' .$$

We must show that there are non-zero real numbers $\lambda_1, \lambda_2, \lambda_3$ and a $g \in GL(V)$ such that:

$$g(\lambda_1 v_1) = v_1'$$

$$g(\lambda_2 v_2) = v_2' \qquad (2.2)$$

$$g(\lambda_3 v_3) = v_3' \quad .$$

As a first rough check of the possibility of the choice of $(g, \lambda_1, \lambda_2, \lambda_3)$, let us count dimensions.

$$\dim G' = 3 \quad .$$

Hence, there are $3 + 1 + 1 + 1 = 6$ parameters available. There are

$$2 + 2 + 2 = 6$$

parameters in the domain space $V \times V \times V$, which just checks.

Here is the proof. First, we can suppose that $(v_1, v_2)$ and $(v_1', v_2')$ are linearly independent. (Otherwise, $(x_1, x_2)$ and $(x_1', x_2')$ would not be two distinct points.) Hence, they form bases of $V \equiv R^2$, and we can first act with $GL(V, R)$ to make them coincide. Thus, we can suppose without loss in generality, that:

$$v_1 = v' \quad ,$$

$$v_2 = v_2' \quad .$$

Suppose:

$$v_3 = av + bv_2$$

(2.3)

$$v_3' = a'v_1 + b'v_2 \quad .$$

Equation (2.2) then takes the form:

$$g(v_1) = \lambda^{-1}{}_1 v_1$$

$$g(v_2) = \lambda_2^{-1} v_2$$

$$g(v_3) = \lambda_3^{-1} v_3 \quad .$$

But, using (2.3),

$$g(v_3) = a\lambda_1^{-1} v_1 + b\lambda_2^{-1} v_2$$

$$= \lambda_3^{-1} a' v_1 + \lambda_3^{-1} b' v_2 \quad ,$$

or

$$a\lambda_1^{-1} = a'\lambda_3^{-1}$$

$$b\lambda_2^{-1} = b'\lambda_3^{-1} \quad .$$

We can then take

$$\lambda_3 = 1 \quad ,$$

and solve for $\lambda_1, \lambda_2$. (Notice that $a \neq 0$, $b \neq 0$, $a' \neq 0$, $b' \neq 0$ is implied by the distinctness of the $(x_1, x_2, x_3)$, $(x_1', x_2', x_3')$.)

Remark. This property of  G'  acting on  R  is called <u>three</u>
<u>point transitivity</u>. Very few finite dimensional transforma-
tion groups can have this sort of "multiple" transitivity on
manifolds.

      This is the end of the multiple transitivity of  G'
on  R.  G'  acting on  R × R × R × R  <u>has</u> algebraic covariants.
      To see this, suppose

$$v_1, v_2, v_3, v_4$$

are four elements of  V'  whose projections

$$x_1, x_2, x_3, x_4$$

in  R  under  π  are distinct points.

      Let

$$\omega \ \varepsilon \ V \wedge V$$

be any fixed non-zero element of the skew-symmetric tensor
product of  V  with itself. (For example, identifying

$$V \ \text{with} \ R^2 \ ,$$

ω  could be taken as  $(1,0) \wedge (0,1)$.)

      For any pair  $(v_1, v_2) \ \varepsilon \ V \times V$,  let  $\omega(v_1, v_2)$  be
the real number such that:

$$v_1 \wedge v_2 \ = \ \omega(v_1, v_2)\omega \qquad\qquad (2.4)$$

Thus, if

$$g \ \varepsilon \ GL(V) \ ,$$

and if

$$g(\omega) \;=\; \det (g)\omega \;\;, \tag{2.5}$$

then:

$$g(v_1) \wedge g(v_2) \;=\; \omega(v_1,v_2)(\det g)\omega \;\;,$$

i.e.,

$$\omega(gv_1,gv_2) \;=\; (\det g)\omega \tag{2.6}$$

Remark. (2.6) indicates that $\omega$ defines what is called a relative invariant in the theory of invariants.

Also,

$$\omega(\lambda_1 v_1, \lambda_2 v_2) \;=\; \lambda_1 \lambda_2 \omega(v_1,v_2) \tag{2.7}$$

$$\text{for } \lambda_1, \lambda_2 \; \varepsilon \; R$$

Now set:

$$h(v_1,v_2,v_3,v_4) \;=\; \omega(v_1,v_2)\omega(v_3,v_4) \tag{2.8}$$

Hence,

$$h(gv_1,gv_2,gv_3,gv_4) \;=\; (\det g)^2 h(v_1,v_2,v_3,v_4) \tag{2.9}$$

$$h(\lambda_1 v_1, \lambda_2 v_2, \lambda_3 v_3, \lambda_4 v_4) \;=\; \lambda_1 \lambda_2 \lambda_3 \lambda_4 h(v_1,v_2,v_3,v_4) \tag{2.10}$$

Now set,

$$f(v_1,v_2,v_3,v_4) \;=\; \frac{h(v_1,v_2,v_3,v_4)}{h(v_1,v_3,v_2,v_4)} \tag{2.11}$$

f   considered as a <u>rational map</u>

$$V \times V \times V \times V \to R$$

(see Volume VIII of IM) is now invariant under two sorts of groups actions.  First, the diagonal action of  G:

$$g(v_1,v_2,v_3,v_4) \;=\; (gv_1,gv_2,gv_3,gv_4)$$

Second, the action of the abelian group

$$R' \times R' \times R' \times R:$$

(R' ≡ multiplicative group of non-zero real numbers.)

$$(\lambda_1,\lambda_2,\lambda_3,\lambda_4)(v_1,v_2,v_3,v_4) \;=\; (\lambda_1 v_1,\lambda_2 v_2,\lambda_3 v_3,\lambda_4 v_4) \quad .$$

The orbit space  R' × R' × R' × R'  is just

$$PS(V) \times PS(V) \times PS(V) \times PS(V) \quad .$$

The function  f  then passes to the quotient to define a rational map

$$PS(V) \times PS(V) \times PS(V) \times PS(V) \to R \quad .$$

This map is <u>invariant under the action of</u>  G.  It is called the <u>cross-ratio map</u>.  In other words, if

$$\pi(v_1) = x_1, \quad \pi(v_2) = x_2,$$

$$\pi(v_3) = x_3, \quad \pi(v_4) = x_4 \quad ,$$

then:

$$f(x_1,x_2,x_3,x_4) \;=\; \frac{h(v_1,v_2,v_3,v_4)}{h(v_1,v_3,v_2,v_4)} \tag{2.12}$$

Let us work this formula out explicitly using the following formulas:

$$v_1 = (y_1, z_1) \ , \qquad x_1 = z_1 y_1^{-1} \ ,$$

etc. (In other words, $V = R^2$.) Then,

$$(v_1, v_2) = \det \begin{pmatrix} y_1 & z_1 \\ y_2 & z_2 \end{pmatrix}$$

$$= y_1 z_2 - z_1 y_2$$

$$= y_1 y_2 (x_2 - x_1)$$

Hence,

$$h(v_1, v_2, v_3, v_4) = y_1 y_2 y_3 y_4 (x_2 - x_1)(x_3 - x_4)$$

$$f(x_1, x_2, x_3, x_4) = \frac{(x_2 - x_1)(x_3 - x_4)}{(x_3 - x_1)(x_2 - x_4)} \qquad (2.13)$$

This is the classical formula for the cross-ratio.

At the other extreme of concreteness, here is a completely coordinate-free and basis independent development.

Let $V$ be a two-dimensional vector space. Let $V \wedge V$ be the exterior product of $V$ with itself. It is a one-dimensional vector space. Let

$$h: V \times V \times V \times V \rightarrow (V \wedge V) \circ (V \wedge V)$$

be the following map:

$$h(v_1,v_2,v_3,v_4) \;\; = \;\; (v_1 \wedge v_2) \circ (v_3 \wedge v_4)$$

( $\circ$  denotes the <u>symmetric tensor product</u>.)

Let

$$f: V \times V \times V \times V \to R$$

be the rational map defined by the following rule:

$$h(v_1,v_2,v_3,v_4) \;\; = \;\; f(v_1,v_2,v_3,v_4)h(v_1,v_3,v_2,v_4) \qquad (2.14)$$

(Notice that  f  is well-defined <u>because</u>

$$(V \wedge V) \circ (V \wedge V)$$

is a one-dimensional vector space.  The analogue of the cross-
ratio for an n-dimensional vector space is to replace  $V \wedge V$ 
by  $V \wedge \cdots \wedge V$ .)  f  now has the required invariance properties
to pass to the quotient to define a rational map

$$PS(V) \times \cdots \times PS(V) \to R$$

which is invariant under the action of  G.

Here is the basic group-theoretic property of the
cross-ratio.

<u>Theorem 2.2</u>.  Let  $(x_1,x_2,x_3,x_4)$ ,  $(x_1',x_2',x_3',x_4')$   be two sets
of four, pairwise distinct, real numbers.  Then one set can
be transformed into the other by the action of the projective
group  G  if and only if:  The value of the cross-ratio is the
same for the two pairs.

The proof is left as an exercise for the reader.

Now, let us turn to the differential invariants.
Let  G  act on  R  via linear fractional transformations, as
before.  Consider another copy of  R  to be considered as a
parameter space, coordinatized by

$$t \ .$$

Let

$$x$$

be the coordinate on the copy of  R  on which  G  acts.  Thus,

$$M(R,R)$$

denotes the space of all maps of the form:

$$t \rightarrow x(t) \ \equiv \ \phi(t)$$

G  acts on  M(R,R)  as follows:

$$g(\phi)(t) \ = \ g(x(t)) \ . \tag{2.15}$$

To keep the notation straight, let

$$R_1 \ = \ \text{space of variable} \ t$$

$$R_2 \ = \ \text{space of variables} \ x \ .$$

Here is one way of looking at the problem:

What are the orbits of  G  acting on
$M(R_1,R_2)$?

To settle this question by Lie's technique, the first step is to find the (possibly non-linear) differential operator

$$\Delta: M(R_1, R_2) \to M(R_1, R_1)$$

which are invariant under the action of G. (The trivial action on $R_1$, the projective action on $R_2$.)

Let $t \to x(t)$ be a curve in R, a,b,c,d constants with ad - bc = 1. Set:

$$y(t) = \frac{ax(t) + b}{cx(t) + d} \tag{2.16}$$

Set

$$y'(t) = \frac{dy}{dt} , \quad x'(t) = \frac{dx}{dt} ,$$

etc.

To find a differential invariant, let us eliminate the constant a,bc from the relations resulting from differentiation of (2.16) three times.

$$y' = \frac{(cx+d)ax' - (ax+b)cx'}{(cx+d)^2}$$

$$= \frac{(ad-bc)x'}{(cx+d)^2}$$

$$= \frac{x'}{(cx+d)^2}$$

Hence,

$$\log y' \ = \ \log x' - 2 \log (cx+d)$$

$$(\log y')' \ \equiv \ \frac{y''}{y'} \ = \ \frac{x''}{x'} - \frac{2c}{cx+d}$$

$$= \ \frac{x''}{x'} - \frac{2}{x + (d/c)}$$

Solve for  $d/c$:

$$\frac{2}{x + (d/c)} \ = \ \frac{x''}{x'} - \frac{y''}{y'} \ = \ \frac{x''y' - x'y''}{x'y'}$$

or

$$\frac{x + (d/c)}{2} \ = \ \frac{x'y'}{x''y' - x'y''}$$

Differentiate once more to eliminate all explicit dependence
on the constants.  The result is the following relation:

$$\frac{y'''}{y'} - \frac{3}{2}\left(\frac{y''}{y'}\right)^2 \ = \ \frac{x'''}{x'} - \frac{3}{2}\left(\frac{x''}{x'}\right)^2 \qquad\qquad (2.17)$$

Now, (2.16) shows that  $t \to x(t)$  and  $t \to y(t)$  are two
curves in  R  which differ by a transformation of  SL(2.R).
The differential expressions on each side of (2.17) are equal.
Define a differential operator

$$\Delta: M(R_1,R_2) \to M(R_1,R_2)$$

by the rule:

$$(\Delta\phi)(t) = \frac{\phi}{\phi'} - \frac{3}{2}\left(\frac{\phi''}{\phi'}\right)^2 \tag{2.18}$$

Theorem 2.3.  $\Delta$, defined by (2.18), is a non-linear third order differential operator  $M(R_1,R_2) \to M(R_1,R_2)$  which is invariant under the action of  $SL(2,R)$  on  $R_2$.  It is called the Schwarzian derivative operator.

It is extremely interesting and important that this Schwarzian derivative also plays a key role in the theory of functions of one complex variable and the theory of automorphic functions.

In this relatively simple case, we can use the Schwarzian derivative to calculate the orbits of  $SL(2,R)$  acting on  $M(R_1,R_2)$.

Theorem 2.4.  For each curve  $\psi$  in  $M(R_1,R_2)$  let

$$\Delta^{-1}(\psi)$$

be its inverse image under the Schwarzian operator  $\Delta$,  i.e., the set of all  $\phi \in M(R_1,R_2)$  such that

$$\Delta\phi = \psi .$$

Then,  $\Delta^{-1}(\psi)$  is an orbit of  $SL(2,R)$  acting on  $M(R_1,R_2)$. Each orbit is of this form.

The proof of this is left to the reader.

Remark. It is possible to relate the algebraic invariant,
i.e., the cross-ratio, to the differential invariant, i.e.,
the Schwarzian. This is described in Chapter 1, p. 23 of
Cartan's book "Theorie des éspaces a connexion projective".
If

$$\phi \in M(R_1, R_2) \quad ,$$

he shows that:

$$(\Delta\phi)(t) = 3 \lim_{h \to 0} \frac{\dfrac{f(\phi(t),\ \phi(t+h),\ \phi(t+2h),\ \phi(t+3h))}{f(t,\ t+h,\ t+2h,\ t+3h)} - 1}{h^2}$$

$$(2.19)$$

where $f(\ ,\ ,\ ,\ )$ is the cross-ratio function. This formula
also exhibits the invariance of $\Delta$ under the action of
$SL(2,R)$ on $M(R_1, R_2)$ in an a priori way (i.e., the formula
only involves invariant objects), and, even better, indicates
a  wider invariance.  In fact, let

$$SL(2,R) \times SL(2,R)$$

act on

$$M(R_1, R_2)$$

as follows:

$$(g_1, g_2)(\phi)(t) = g_1 \phi(g_2^{-1} t))$$

$$\text{for } g_1, g_2 \in SL(2, R) \quad .$$

Since the cross-ratio is invariant under $SL(2, R)$, we see from formula (2.19) that:

$\Delta$ is invariant under the action of
$SL(2, R) \times SL(2, R)$ on $M(R_1, R_2)$, i.e.,

$$\Delta((g_1, g_2)(\phi)) = \Delta(\phi) \qquad (2.20)$$

$$\text{for } g_1, g_2 \in SL(2, R) \quad .$$

As Cartan briefly indicates, another approach to the projective differential geometry of curves is to relate it to theory of linear differential equations. This approach is developed in detail in Wilczynski's book "Projective differential geometry". In fact, Wilczynski develops the whole theory using Lie's ideas in a very direct way, particularly the invariant theory of infinite Lie groups.

I will now turn to consideration of this approach.


3.      THE INFINITE LIE GROUP WHICH PRESERVES THE CLASS OF
        LINEAR DIFFERENTIAL OPERATORS

In Wilczynski's book "Projective differential geometry of curves and ruled surfaces" one sees a classic and brillant example of Lie's ideas used both for analytic purposes (to

study time-dependent ordinary differential equations) and for
geometric purposes (to study curves and surfaces in projective
spaces). This material has extensive ramifications in modern
mathematics, physics and engineering. In this section I
present an "algebrazation" of Wilczynski's ideas, involving
the purely algebraic theory of linear differential operators
presented in GPS, Chapter I.

Let $F$ be a commutative, associative algebra over
the real numbers. (In applications, $F$ will be the algebra
of $C^{\infty}$ functions on a manifold. In Wilczynski's case,
$F$ = space of functions of a real variable $x$.)

Let $\Gamma$ and $\Gamma'$ be F-modules. Let

$$\Delta: \Gamma \to \Gamma'$$

be an R-linear mapping.

For $f \varepsilon F$, set

$$\sigma(f,\Delta)(\gamma) = \Delta(f\gamma) - f\Delta(\gamma) \qquad (3.1)$$

for $\gamma \varepsilon \Gamma$

$\sigma(f,\Delta)$ is also an R-linear map $: \Gamma \to \Gamma$. Iterate the
construction:

$$\sigma(f_1,f_2,\Delta) = \sigma(f_1,\sigma(f_2,\Delta))$$

$$\vdots$$

Definition. $\Delta$ is an n-th order linear differential operator : $\Gamma \to \Gamma'$ if the following condition is satisfied:

$$\sigma(f_1, \ldots, f_{n+1}, \Delta) = 0 \tag{3.2}$$

$$\text{for } f_1, \ldots, f_{n+1} \in F .$$

Let

$$D^n(\Gamma, \Gamma')$$

denote the set of such n-th order differential operators. (From now on in this section when I use the term "differential operator" I always mean "linear differential operator".)

An R-linear map : $\Gamma \to \Gamma'$ is a differential operator if it belongs to $D^n(\Gamma, \Gamma')$, for some n. Let $D(\Gamma, \Gamma')$ denote the set of such operators. It has an ascending filtration;

$$D^0(\Gamma, \Gamma') \subset D^1(\Gamma, \Gamma') \subset \cdots \subset D(\Gamma, \Gamma') .$$

($D^0(\Gamma, \Gamma')$ denotes the space of F-linear maps $\Gamma \to \Gamma'$.)

Now, following Lie and Wilczynski, we introduce "symmetries". Algebraically, they may be described as follows:

Definition. An automorphism of the F-module $\Gamma$ is a pair $(\alpha, \beta)$ where

$$\beta: F \to F$$

is an automorphism of the algebra F, and

$$\alpha: \Gamma \to \Gamma$$

is a map such that:

$$\alpha(f\gamma) = \beta(f)\alpha(\gamma) \tag{3.3}$$

for $f \in F$, $\gamma \in \Gamma$ .

The set of such automorphisms forms a group, that we denote by

$$\text{Aut } (\Gamma) \quad .$$

Thus an element

$$g \in \text{Aut } (\Gamma)$$

is a pair $(\alpha, \beta) \equiv g$ with properties described above.

Similarly,

$$\text{Aut } (\Gamma')$$

denotes the group of automorphisms of $\Gamma'$.

Given

$$\Delta \in D^n(\Gamma, \Gamma') \quad ,$$

$$(g', g) \in \text{Aut } (\Gamma') \times \text{Aut } (\Gamma) \quad ,$$

set:

$$(g', g)(\Delta)(\gamma) = g'\Delta(g^{-1}\gamma)) \quad . \tag{3.3}$$

Theorem 3.1. $(g',g)(\Delta)$, defined by formula (3.4), is again an n-th order linear differential operator : $\Gamma \to \Gamma'$. In particular, $(g',g)$ acts as an automorphism of the F-module

$$D^n(\Gamma,\Gamma') \quad .$$

Proof. For $f \in F$,

$$\sigma(f,(g',g)(\Delta))(\gamma) \;=\; (g',g)(\Delta)(g\gamma) \,-\, f(g',g)(\Delta)(\gamma)$$

$$=\; g'\Delta(g^{-1}(f\gamma)) \,-\, f(g'\Delta(g^{-1}\gamma)) \qquad (3.5)$$

Suppose that:

$$g \;=\; (\alpha,\beta)$$

$$g' \;=\; (\alpha',\beta') \quad .$$

Then,

$$g(f\gamma) \;=\; \beta(f)\alpha(\gamma)$$

Hence,

$$g^{-1}(\beta(f)\alpha(\gamma)) \;=\; f\gamma$$

Hence,

$$g^{-1}(f\gamma) \;=\; \beta^{-1}(f)\alpha^{-1}(\gamma) \quad .$$

Thus,

$$g^{-1} \;=\; (\alpha^{-1},\beta^{-1}) \qquad (3.6)$$

Inset (3.6) into (3.5):

$$\sigma(f,(g,g')(\Delta))(\gamma) = g'\Delta(\beta^{-1}(f)\alpha^{-1}(\gamma)) - fg'\Delta(\alpha^{-1}(\gamma))$$

$$= g'(\sigma(\beta^{-1}(f),\Delta)(\alpha^{-1}(\gamma)) + \beta^{-1}(f)\Delta(\alpha^{-1}(\gamma))$$

$$- fg'\Delta(\alpha^{-1}(\gamma))$$

$$= g'(\sigma(\beta^{-1}(f),\Delta)(\alpha^{-1}(\gamma)) + \beta'\beta^{-1}(f)\alpha'\Delta\alpha^{-1}(\gamma)$$

$$- f2\Delta\alpha^{-1}(\gamma)$$

$$(3.7)$$

<u>Theorem 3.2</u>. Suppose that $g = (\alpha,\beta) \in \text{Aut } \Gamma$, $g' = (\alpha',\beta')$ $\in \text{Aut } \Gamma'$ satisfies the following condition:

$$\beta = \beta' \qquad\qquad (3.8)$$

Then, if $\Delta \in D^r(\Gamma,\Gamma')$, $(g,g')(\Delta)$ is also an r-th order differential operator, and:

$$\sigma(f_1,\dots,f_s; (g,g')(\Delta)) = g'\sigma(\beta^{-1}f_1,\dots,\beta^{-1}f_s; \Delta)g^{-1}$$
$$\text{for } s = 1,2,\dots; \quad f_1,\dots,f_s \in F \ . \qquad (3.9)$$

<u>Proof</u>. Formula (3.9) is proved for $s = 1$ by (3.7), and for general $s$ by induction.

That

$$(g,g')(\Delta) \in D^r(\Gamma,\Gamma')$$

follows readily from formula (3.9) and the hypothesis.

Consider the subgroup of the

$$(g,g') \in (Aut\ \Gamma) \times (Aut\ \Gamma')$$

which satisfy condition (3.8), i.e., g and g' <u>act in the
same way</u> on the algebra F. Denote this group by W, and call
it the <u>Wilczynski group</u>. By Theorem 3.2, this group acts as a
group of automorphisms of the F-module

$$D^r(\Gamma,\Gamma') \quad .$$

It is this action (in the special case where F = algebra of $C^\infty$
functions of one real or complex variable) which is basic to
Wilczynski's method for dealing with projective differential
geometry. In fact, W is an <u>infinite Lie group</u>, acting on
$D^r(\Gamma,\Gamma')$, and Wilczynski's method involved finding the <u>invari-
ants</u> (and <u>covariants</u>) of W acting on these modules.

One can now define a subgroup of W called the <u>gauge
transformation subgroup</u>, as the set of all

$$g = (\alpha,\beta)$$

with

$$\beta = identity \quad .$$

In other words, g is a map $\Gamma \to \Gamma$ such that

$$g(f\gamma) = fg(\gamma)$$

$$for\ f \in F,\ \gamma \in \Gamma \quad .$$

(The name "gauge transformation" comes, of course, from physics.
See my books, LGP, LAQM, VB and GPS, for details.)  This subgroup is an invariant subgroup of  W.  Wilczynski's method
for finding invariants for  W  is first to find the invariants
of the gauge transformation subgroup, then to see how these
transform under automorphisms of  F.  The objects invariant
under gauge transformations (but not necessarily the full
group  W) are called semi-invariants.

Let us now turn from this very general setting to an
example which connects these very general ideas to the
Schwarzian derivative.


4.        THE SCHWARTZIAN DERIVATIVE AS DIFFERENTIAL INVARIANTS
          OF THE WILCZYNSKI GROUP

Specialize the general setting of Section 3 as follows:
$\Gamma' = \Gamma = F = F(R) \equiv C^{\infty}$  functions of a real variable  x.  In
order to keep as close as possible to the classical notation
(as in Wilczynski [1]), we denote an element of  F  by "y".
$y', y'', \ldots$  denotes, as usual, the derivatives of  y  as a
function of  x.

Suppose that:

$$\Delta(y) = y'' + 2ay' + by , \qquad (4.1)$$

with  $a, b \in F$.  We see that  $\Delta$  is a second order linear differ
ential operator.

Set:

$$\phi(\Delta) = b - a^2 - a' \tag{4.2}$$

Theorem 4.1. $\phi$, as a map

$$D^2(F,F) \to F$$

is a semi-invariant of the Wilczynski group, i.e.,

$$\phi(g(\Delta)) = \phi(\Delta) \tag{4.3}$$

for all $g \in W$

which is a pure gauge transformation.

Proof. Each gauge transformation $g$ is of the following form:

$$g(y) = f^{-1}y \quad , \tag{4.4}$$

for fixed $f \in F$, all $y \in F$ .

Thus,

$$g(\Delta)(y) = f^{-1}\Delta(fy)$$

$$= f^{-1}(\sigma(\Delta,f) + f\Delta(y))$$

$$= f^{-1}\sigma(\Delta,f)(y) + \Delta(y) \quad ,$$

or

$$g(\Delta) = f^{-1}\sigma(\Delta,f) + \Delta \tag{4.5}$$

(This is obviously a general algebraic relation, which plays
the key role in Wilczynski's work.)

Now,

$$\Delta(fy) = (fy)'' + 2a(fy)' + bfy$$

$$= f''y + 2f'y' + fy'' + 2af'y + 2afy' + bf'y$$

Hence,

$$\sigma(\Delta,f)(y) \equiv \Delta(fy) - f\Delta(y) = f''y + 2f'y' + 2af'y \quad (4.6)$$

Suppose:

$$g(\Delta)(y) = y'' + 2a_1y' + b_1y \quad .$$

We can now read off from (4.4) and (4.5) the values of $a_1, b_1$:

$$a_1 = a + f^{-1}f'$$

$$b_1 = b + f^{-1}f' + 2af^{-1}f1 \quad (4.7)$$

Remark. This is an example of a "prolonged action" of an
infinite Lie group. For each $f \in F$, formulas (4.7) define
a map

$$(x,a,b) \rightarrow (x,a_1,b_1)$$

of $R^3 \rightarrow R^3$.

These sort of formulas also occur in physics. See LAQM.

We can now prove (4.1), the invariance equation:

$$\phi(g(\Delta)) = b_1 - a_1^2 - a_1'$$

$$= \quad, \text{ using } (4.6),$$

$$b + f''f^{-1} + 2af^{-1}f' - (a+f^{-1}f')^2 - (a+f^{-1}f')^1$$

$$= b + f''f^{-1} + 2af^{-1}f' - a^2 - 2af^{-1}f' - f^{-2}(f')^2$$

$$- a^1 + f^{-2}(f')^2 - f^{-1}f''$$

$$= b - a^2 - a'$$

$$= \phi(\Delta)$$

This proves formula (4.3) and Theorem 4.1.

Remark. This gives a beautiful and important example of a "differential invariant", in the sense of Lie!

Now, let us relate the semi-invariant

$$\phi(\Delta)$$

to the Schwarzian.

First, we see from (4.6) that the gauge transformation g can be chosen so that:

$$a_1 = 0 \quad.$$

This means that we can suppose (after a gauge transformation) that $\Delta$ has the following <u>canonical form</u>:

$$\Delta(y) = y'' + by \qquad (4.8)$$

<u>Remark</u>. The gauge transformation leading to the canonical form (4.8) is classically called the <u>Liouville transformation</u>. Its properties are very important in the study of the asymptotic behavior of second order, linear, time-dependent, ordinary differential equations. In this case, the invariant $\Delta$ takes the form:

$$\phi(\Delta) = b \quad . \qquad (4.9)$$

<u>Theorem 4.2</u>. Let $y_1, y_2$ be two linearly independent solutions of the differential equation

$$\Delta(y) = 0 \quad .$$

Construct the map

$$x \to z(x) = \frac{y_2(x)}{y_1(x)} \qquad (4.10)$$

Then, $\phi(\Delta) = 1/2$ (the Schwarzian of $z$.)

> <u>Proof</u>. A gauge transformation is of the form
>
> $$y \to fy \quad .$$

Hence, it does not affect the map $z$ of $R \to R$. We can then suppose without loss of generality that $\Delta$ takes its canonical form, i.e.,

$$\phi(\Delta) = b \quad .$$

Thus we have:

$$y_1'' + by_1 = 0$$
$$y_2'' + by_2 = 0$$

(4.11)

Let $z$ be defined by (4.10). The <u>Schwarzian</u> of $z$ is:

$$\frac{z'''}{z'} - \frac{3}{2} \left(\frac{z''}{z'}\right)^2 \equiv s(z) \quad .$$

(4.12)

Set:

$$w = \log z'$$

(4.13)

Then,

$$w' = \frac{z''}{z'}$$

$$w'' = \frac{z'''}{z'} - \frac{(z'')^2}{(z')^2}$$

Hence,

$$s(z) = w'' - \frac{1}{2} \left(\frac{z''}{z'}\right)^2$$

$$= w'' - \frac{1}{2} (w')^2$$

(4.14)

Remark. Formula (4.14) gives the relation between the Schwarzian and the Riccatti equation. For, if one wants to solve the differential equation

$$s(z) = h(x) \quad ,$$

with a known function $h(x)$, (4.14) shows that it can be solved by first solving the Riccatti equation

$$u' - \frac{1}{2} u^2 = h(x) \quad ,$$

for $u(x)$, then setting:

$$w = \int u \ dx \quad ,$$

$$z = \int e^w \ dx \quad .$$

Return to the proof of Theorem 4.2. Define $z$ by (4.10). Then,

$$z' = \frac{y_1 y_2' - y_2 y_1'}{y_1^2}$$

$$w \equiv \log z' = \log (y_1 y_2' - y_2 y_1') - 2 \log y_1 \quad .$$

Now,

$$(y_1 y_2' - y_2 y_1')' = y_1' y_2' - y_1 y_2'' - y_2' y_1' - y_2' y_1'$$

$$= 0$$

because $y_1, y_2$ satisfy (4.11). Hence,

$$w' = -\frac{2y_1'}{y_1}$$

$$w'' = \frac{2(y_1')^2}{y_1^2} - \frac{2y_1''}{y_1}$$

$$= \frac{2(y_1')^2}{y_1^2} + 2b$$

$$= \frac{1}{2}(w')^2 + 2b \quad ,$$

or

$$w'' - \frac{1}{2}(w')^2 = 2b \equiv \phi(\Delta)$$

This finishes the proof of Theorem 4.2.

Thus, we see that there are two ways of understanding the Schwarzian--as a differential invariant of $SL(2,R)$ acting on $R$, and also as a differential invariant of an <u>infinite</u> Lie group, namely the gauge transformation subgroup of the Wilcyznski group. Presumably, there are vast generalizations of these facts, but--to my knowledge--they have never been worked out.

5.    THE METHOD OF SEMI-INVARIANTS IN INVARIANT THEORY

There is an abstract pattern to these ideas which it
is worthwhile to isolate.  Let  A  be a set, and let  G  be
a transformation group acting on  A.  An invariant of  G  is
a map

$$f: A \to C$$

such that:

$$f(ga) = f(a) \qquad\qquad (5.1)$$

for all  $g \in G$,  $a \in A$  .

(C  denotes the complex numbers.  Other fields would do as
well.)  In words, (5.1) says that  f  is a complex-valued
function on  A  which is invariant under the action of  G.

Here is a method that is frequently used in the classical literature, particularly by Lie.  Pick a subgroup  H  of
G.  Study the invariants of  H.  (They are called the semi-
invariants of  G.)  Then, study how  G  acts on the semi-
invariants.

For example, if  H  is an invariant subgroup of  G,
then  G  maps a semi-invariant into another semi-invariant.
To see this, suppose that  f  is a semi-invariant, i.e.,

$$f(ha) = f(a) \qquad\qquad (5.2)$$

for  $h \in H$,  $a \in A$  .

Let $g(f)$ denote the transform of $f$ by $g \in G$:

$$g(f)(a) = f(g^{-1}a) .$$

Then,

$$g(f)(ha) = f(g^{-1}ha)$$

$$= f(g^{-1}hg)(g^{-1}a)$$

$$= f(g^{-1}a) ,$$

using the fact that $g^{-1}hg \in H$ and (5.2) ,

$$g(f)(ha) = g(f)(a)$$

Clearly, Wilczynski's work involves this situation.
A = set of linear differential operators, G = group of
linear module automorphisms, H = group of "pure" gauge transformations.

Another relevant situation is the classical algebraic
invariant theory. (For example, see Chapter 23 of Lie and
Scheffer's "Vorlesungen über Continuerliche Gruppen".) Here
is one interesting situation.

$$G = SL(2,C)$$

$$A = (\underbrace{C^2 \circ \cdots \circ C^2}_{n \text{ copies}})$$

G acts on A via its natural linear action. (A can also be identified with the space of n-th degree homogeneous polynomials in two complex variables $x_1, x_2$.) _Invariants_ are then "rational" maps f: A → C invariant under the action of G, in the sense of (5.1).

Take H as the subgroup of matrices of the form

$$\begin{pmatrix} a & b \\ 0 & a^{-1} \end{pmatrix}$$

Rational maps f: A → C invariant under H are called _semi_-invariants. Note that H is, in this case, _not_ an invariant subgroup of G. It is, however, a _maximal solvable_ subgroup. (In this form, the idea generalizes to study invariants of GL(m,C) for m ≥ 3.)

I mean to return later to a study of these general ideas. There are close relations to the theory of "induced represen-tations".

Chapter C

INTEGRAL INVARIANTS


1.  INTRODUCTION

Among Lie's last works were several papers on what
he called Integral Invariants.  (See Vol. VI of his
Collected Works.)  Presumably, their theory stands in
relation to differential invariants as integration stands
to differentiation.  In this chapter I give a brief
introduction and modern development of some of these
ideas.

In fact, we shall see that what Lie meant by an
"integral invariant" is the same as what one would call
a Lagrangian in a general calculus-of-variations setting.
Thus, in modern terms, Lie deals with a calculus of
variations problem with a given group of automorphisms.
In turn, this leads one immediately into many sorts of
physics and engineering problems, as I have tried to show
in my own books.

It is particularly important to keep in mind that
Lie means to stay on a sufficiently general level to cover
cases of invariance under finite or infinite transformation groups.  This topic leads one immediately into
modern elementary particle physics.  For example, the

187

theory of "gauge fields" involves study of field theoretic
Lagrangians which are invariant under abelian or non-
abelian gauge transformations.  (Maxwell electrodynamics
is an example of a theory with an abelian gauge transformation symmetry.  The Yang-Mills field is an example
of a field theory with a non-abelian gauge symmetry.  (See
Vol. X of IM and GPS.)

The theory of integral invariants also has wide
ramifications in Classical Mechanics and Integral Geometry.
For mechanics, the classical sources are Poincaré's
"Mecanique Céleste" and Cartan's "Lecons sur les invariants intégraux".  These ideas have been recently revived
under the slogan "Application of symplectic manifold
theory to mechanics".  (See Abraham-Marsden [1] for an
introduction.)

Another branching into modern mathematics leads to
Integral Geometry.  (There are no adequate modern introductory treatises.  See Blaschke [1] and Santalo [1] for
brief descriptions of some of the geometric ideas in a
classical framework.  See Federer [1] for one modern
treatment of the underlying measure theoretic foundation.)
Roughly, this involves the calculation and study of properties of integrals involving quantities of "geometric"
interest, such as "lengths", "areas", "volumes", etc.

In this chapter I will also take the opportunity
to put some of the ideas scattered throughout my own
books into a more definitive differential-geometric form.


## 2.    LAGRANGIANS FOR FIBER SPACES

Let

$$\pi: Y \to X$$

be a submersion mapping between manifolds.  (Recall this
means that  $\pi_*: T(Y) \to T(X)$  is onto.)  We shall say
that the triple

$$(Y, X, \pi)$$

forms a fiber space, with  Y  total space,  X  as base
space,  $\pi$  as projection map.

Definition.  A tangent covector  $\theta$  to a point of  Y  is
said to be base-like (relative to the fiber space) if
there is a covector  $\theta'$  to  X  such that

$$\pi^*(\theta') = \theta .$$


Remark.  A differential form  $\theta$  on  Y  can have the
property that is value  $\theta(y)$  at each point  y  of  Y
is base-like without the form itself being base-like, i.e.,
the pull-back of a form on  X.  To see this, consider:

$$Y = \text{space of variables } (x,y) \equiv R^2$$

$$X = \text{space of variable } x \equiv R'$$

$$\pi(x,y) = x \quad .$$

Any form of the type

$$\theta = a(x,y)dx$$

obviously has this property.

The necessary and sufficient condition that a $\theta$ which is base-like for each $y \in Y$ be the pull-back of a form on $X$ is that $d\theta$ be base-like for each $y \in Y$.

Definition. Suppose

$$\dim X = n \quad .$$

A Lagrangian for the fiber space

$$(Y,X,\pi)$$

is defined as an n-form $L$ on $Y$ whose value at each point is base-like.


3.    LAGRANGIANS AND VARIATIONAL PROBLEMS FOR MAPPING
      ELEMENT SPACES

Specialize the situation considered in Section 2. Let $X$ and $Z$ be manifolds, and let $r$ be a positive integer. Suppose that an orientation is fixed for $X$.

(See   DGCV.)   Let

$$M^r(X,Z)$$

denote the space of r-th order mapping elements of mappings
: $X \to Z$.

$M^r(X,Z)$   is a fiber space over   X.

A Lagrangian for this fiber space (in the sense defined
in Section 2) is an r-th order Lagrangian  L  for the
space of mappings  $X \to Z$.

Let

$$M(X,Z)$$

denote the space of mappings  $X \to Z$.  The Lagrangian  L
defines a function

$$\underset{\sim}{L}: M(X,Z) \to R$$

by means of the following formula:

$$\underset{\sim}{L}(\phi) = \int_X (\partial^r \phi)^*(L) \qquad (3.1)$$

for each  $\phi \in M(X,Z)$  .

The data

$$(X,Z,L,\underset{\sim}{L})$$

is said to define a variational problem.

Such a variational problem is said to be homogeneous
if the map  $\phi \to \underset{\sim}{L}(\phi)$  is independent of the parameterization

<u>of</u>  $\phi$.  This means that, for each diffeomorphism

$$\alpha: X \rightarrow X \quad,$$

$$\underset{\sim}{L}(\phi) \;=\; \underset{\sim}{L}(\phi\alpha) \quad. \tag{3.2}$$

The notion of <u>extremals</u> of such variational problems
(which are maps  $\phi: X \rightarrow Z$) is now defined as usual in
terms of deformation of  $\phi$.

<u>Remarks</u>.  The integral on the right hand side of (3.1) is
to be taken as the integral of the n-form <u>relative to the</u>
<u>given orientation of</u>  X.  (See DGCV, Chapter 7.)

Of course, one must also worry about <u>convergence</u> of
these integrals.  It is traditional to work in a "formal"
way and not worry about such problems.  Actually, in
various disciplines (e.g., quantum field theory and
"infinite time horizon" growth theory in economics) it <u>is</u>
an important question.  Someday I hope to develop the
question more seriously.

Here is what is involved in more traditional language,
in terms of coordinate systems for  X  and  Z.

Let

$$x \;=\; (x^i)$$

$$z \;=\; (z^a)$$

be coordinate systems for  X  and  Z.  Let

$$(x, z, \partial z, \partial^2 z, \ldots)$$

denote the corresponding <u>Lie coordinates</u> for $M^r(X,Z)$.

A Lagrangian is then of the form:

$$L(x, z, \partial z, \ldots) dx^1 \wedge \cdots \wedge dx^n$$

If $x \to z(x)$ are coordinates of a map $\phi$, then

$$\underset{\sim}{L}(\phi) \;=\; \int L(x, z(x), \partial z(x), \ldots, \partial^r z(x)) \; dx_1, \ldots, dx_n \quad (3.3)$$

which is, of course, the traditional form in which one
sees calculus of variations problems in the classical
literature.

## 4.   SYMMETRIES (IN THE SENSE OF LIE) OF VARIATIONAL
      PROBLEMS

Let $(X, Z, M^r(X,Z), L, \underset{\sim}{L})$ be, as in previous sections,
data which define a <u>variational problem</u>.

Let $P$ be the $F(M^r(X,Z))$-module of one-differential
forms on $M^r(X,Z)$ which defines the <u>contact structure</u>.
The prolongation maps

$$\partial^r \phi : X \to M^r(X,Z)$$

associated with maps $\phi \in M(X,Z)$ then satisfy

$$(\partial^r \phi)^*(P) \;=\; 0 \quad,$$

i.e., are <u>solution submanifolds</u> of $P$.

In terms of the Lie coordinate systems

$$(x, z, \partial z, \ldots)$$

for $M^r(X,Z)$. P is generated by the one-forms:

$$dz - (\partial z)dx$$

$$d(\partial z) - (\partial^2 z)dx$$

$$\vdots$$

Definition. A diffeomorphism

$$\alpha: M^r(X,Z) \rightarrow M^r(X,Z)$$

is a contact automorphism if:

$$\alpha^*(P) = P \qquad\qquad (4.1)$$

Given a map

$$\beta: X \times Z \rightarrow X \times Z \quad,$$

there is a unique contact automorphism

$$\beta^r: M^r(X,Z) \rightarrow M^r(X,Z) \quad,$$

such that the following diagram of mappings is commutative:

$$
\begin{array}{ccc}
M^r(X,Z) & \xrightarrow{\ \beta^r\ } & M^r(X,Z) \\
\downarrow & & \downarrow \\
X \times Z & \xrightarrow{\hspace{2cm}} & X \times Z
\end{array}
\qquad (4.2)
$$

(The vertical arrows in (4.2) denote the usual projection maps.) $\beta^r$ is called the <u>prolongation</u> of $\beta$.

<u>Definition</u>. A diffeomorphism

$$\beta: X \times Z \to X \times Z$$

is a <u>symmetry</u> (in Lie's sense) of the variational problem if the following condition is satisfied:

$$\int_X (\partial^r \phi)^*(\beta^r)^*(L) = \underset{\sim}{L}(\phi) \tag{4.3}$$

$$\text{for all} \quad \phi \ \epsilon \ M(X,Z) \quad .$$

<u>Definition</u>. Let G be a group of diffeomorphisms of $X \ \epsilon \ Z$. A Lagrangian L on $M^r(X,Z)$ is said to be an <u>integral invariant</u> for G if each $\beta \ \epsilon \ G$ acts as a symmetry of the variational problem defined by L.

Let us now descend from this general framework to study a classical special case.

5.      SYMMETRIES OF LAGRANGIANS OF THE FORM $\int L(x,y,y')\ dx$

Specialize the general situation described in Section 2 so that both domains and ranges of mappings are the real numbers. To keep to the classical notation, let

$X \equiv$ space of variable $x$

be the domain,

$Y =$ space of variable $y$

be the range. For simplicity, consider only first order Lagrangians. Hence,

$r = 1$ .

$M^1(X,Y)$ has coordinates

$(x,y,y')$ .

$y'$ is identified with $dy/dx$. In words, if

$x \to y(x)$

is a map

$\phi: X \to Y$ ,

then

$\partial^1\phi: X \to M^1(X,Y)$

is the map

$$x \to \left( x, y(x), y'(x) \equiv \frac{dy}{dx} \right) .$$

Another way of putting it is to say that $y'$ is the function on $M^1(X,Y)$ such that

$\theta = dy - y'dx$

generates the contact Pfaffian system on $M^1(X,Y)$.

A <u>Lagrangian</u> is an object of the form

$$L(x,y,y')dx \quad . \tag{5.1}$$

If

$$\phi \in M(X,Y)$$

is given by a map

$$x \rightarrow y(x) \quad ,$$

then

$$\underset{\sim}{L}(\phi) \;=\; \int L\left(x, y(x),\, \frac{dy}{dx}\right)\, dx \quad . \tag{5.2}$$

To investigate the invariance properties of L under diffeomorphisms of $X \times Y$, it is convenient to "homogenize" the integral (5.2). Here is how to do it. Let

$$Z \;=\; X \times Y$$

$$T \;=\; \text{space of variable } t \;\equiv\; R \quad .$$

Consider

$$M^1(T,Z) \quad ,$$

with Lie coordinate system

$$(t,x,y,\dot{x},\dot{y})$$

Thus, if

$$t \rightarrow (x(t),\, y(t))$$

is a map $T \rightarrow Z$, then the coordinates of its prolongation are:

$$t \rightarrow \left(t, \; x(t), \; y(t), \; \dot{x}(t) \equiv \frac{dx}{dt}, \; \dot{y}(t) \equiv \frac{dy}{dt}\right) \; .$$

Consider a Lagrangian  L'  of  (T,Z),  of the form:

$$L' \; = \; L'(x,y,t,\dot{x},\dot{y}) dt \quad .$$

Given a map

$$\psi: \; T \rightarrow Z$$

defined by functions

$$t \rightarrow (x(t), \; y(t)) \; \equiv \; \psi(t) \quad ,$$

set:

$$L'(\psi) \; = \; \int L'\left(x(t), \; y(t), \; t \; \frac{dx}{dt}, \; \frac{dy}{dt}\right) \; dt \quad . \tag{5.3}$$

The conditions that the integral on the right hand side of (5.3) be independent of the parameterization are then that:

$$L' \; \text{is independent of} \; t. \tag{5.4}$$

$$L'(x,y,\lambda\dot{x},\lambda\dot{y}) \; = \; \lambda L(x,y,\dot{x},\dot{y}) \tag{5.5}$$

$$\text{for} \; \lambda \; \epsilon \; R, \; \lambda > 0 \quad .$$

Given

$$\phi: \; X \rightarrow Y \quad ,$$

we can construct its graph

$$gr(\phi): X \to Z$$

<u>Definition</u>. A function $L': T(Z) \to R$ satisfying (3.3)
is the <u>homogenized version of the Lagrangian</u> $L$ <u>if</u>:

$$\underset{\sim}{L}'(\text{graph } \phi) = \underset{\sim}{L}(\phi) \tag{5.6}$$

$$\text{for all } \phi \in M(X,Y) \quad .$$

(5.6) then requires that:

$$\int L'\left(x, \ y(x), \ 1, \ \frac{dy}{dx}\right) dx = \int L\left(x, \ y(x), \ \frac{dy}{dx}\right) dx \tag{5.7}$$

for each function $x \to y(x)$.

Condition (4.7) is implied by the following condition:

$$L'(x,y,1,y') = L(x,y,y') \tag{5.8}$$

(5.8) combined with (5.5) implies that:

$$L'(x,y,\dot{x},\dot{y}) = L\left(x, \ y, \ \frac{\dot{y}}{\dot{x}}\right) \dot{x} \tag{5.9}$$

Conversely, formula (5.9) can be used to <u>define</u> $L'$
in terms of $L$.

Let

$$\beta: X \times Y \to X \times Y$$

be a diffeomorphism. The condition that $\beta$ is a <u>symmetry</u>
is that:

$$\int L' \left( \psi(t), \frac{d\psi}{dt} \right) dt = \int L' \left( \alpha(\psi(t)), \frac{d}{dt} \beta(\psi(t)) \right) dt \quad (5.10)$$

for each map

$$\psi: R \rightarrow X \times Y \quad .$$

Condition (5.10) means that:

$$\int \psi^*((\beta^1)^*(L')) dt = \int \psi^*(L') dt \quad (5.11)$$

for each map

$$\psi: R \rightarrow X \times Y \quad .$$

Using (5.11) and the relation between the prolongation

$$\beta^1: M^1(X,Y) \rightarrow M^1(X,Y) \quad ,$$

we see that condition (5.11) is equivalent to:

$$\int (\partial^1 \phi)^*((\beta^1)^*(L \ dx)) = \int (\partial^1 \phi^*)(L \ dx) \quad (5.12)$$

for each map

$$\phi: X \rightarrow Y \quad .$$

This is the condition given in Section 2.

Example.  Arc-length in the plane and its covariance under
          rotations.

    Set

$$L' = \sqrt{\dot{x}^2 + \dot{y}^2}$$

It clearly satisfies the homogeneity condition (3.3).  If

$$t \rightarrow (x(t), y(t)) \quad = \quad \psi(t) \ , \qquad a \leq t \leq h$$

is a curve in $R^2$, then

$$\int_a^b \ L' \left( x(t), \ y(t), \ \frac{dx}{dt} \ , \ \frac{dy}{dt} \right) \ dt$$

$$= \quad \text{arc-length of the curve.}$$

We can also write $L'$ in non-homogeneous form.
Suppose the curve is parameterized as

$$x \rightarrow (x, \ y(x))$$

Then,

$$\text{arc-length} \quad = \quad \int_a^b \ \sqrt{1 + (y')^2} \ \ dx$$

Thus,

$$L \quad = \quad \sqrt{1 + y'^2} \ \ dx \tag{5.13}$$

is a Lagrangian on

$$M^1(X,Y) \quad .$$

Consider a diffeomorphism

$$\beta \colon X \times Y \rightarrow X \times Y$$

which is a <u>rotation</u> of $R^2$.  We know, geometrically, that
it leaves arc-length invariant.  Let us verify this fact

by following Lie's procedure, i.e., computing the prolongation

$$\beta^1 : M^1(X,Y) \to M^1(X,Y) \quad ,$$

and calculating its effect on

L  .

β  is of the form

$$\beta(x,y) = (x \cos \theta + y \sin \theta, - x \sin \theta + y \cos \theta)$$

for some angle  θ.

Hence,

$$\beta^*(x) = x \cos \theta + y \sin \theta$$

$$\beta^*(y) = -x \sin \theta + y \cos \theta$$

We can compute the prolongation  $\beta^1$  by requiring
that it be a contact transformation, i.e., preserve the
contact ideal.  This means that it <u>preserves the contact</u>
<u>form</u>

$$dy - y' \, dx \quad .$$

up to a factor.  This can be done in the simplest computa-
tional way by playing with differentials, in the following
style:

$$y' = \frac{dy}{dx} \qquad\qquad (5.14)$$

$$(\beta^1)*(y') \;=\; \frac{d(\beta*(y))}{d(\beta*(x))}$$

$$=\; \frac{-\sin\,\theta\,dx\,+\,\cos\,\theta\,dy}{\cos\,\theta\,dx\,+\,\sin\,\theta\,dy}$$

$$=\; \text{, using } (5.14),$$

$$=\; \frac{-\sin\,\theta\,+\,\cos\,\theta\,y'}{\cos\,\theta\,+\,\sin\,\theta\,y'} \qquad (5.15)$$

Remark.  Formula (5.15) is familiar in physics (e.g., in Special Relativity) as the Law of Transformation of Velocities under Lorentz Transformation.  (In this case, $x = t \equiv$ time,  $y \equiv$ space variable,  $\theta$  is pure imaginary.)

Using (5.15) and (5.13) we now have:

$$(\beta^1)*(1+(y')^2) \;=\; 1\,+\,\left(\frac{\cos\,\theta\,y'\,-\,\sin\,\theta}{\cos\,\theta\,+\,\sin\,\theta\,y'}\right)^2$$

$$=\; \frac{1\,+\,y'^2}{(\cos\,\theta\,+\,\sin\,\theta\,y')^2}$$

$$(\beta^1)*(dx) \;=\; \cos\,\theta\,dx\,+\,\sin\,\theta\,dy$$

$$\equiv\; (\cos\,\theta\,+\,y'\,\sin\,\theta)dx\,+\,\sin\,\theta\,(dy-y'dx)$$

Hence,

$$(\beta^1)^*(L) \quad = \quad (1+y'^2)^{1/2} \; dx + \text{a multiple of } (dy-y'dx)$$

Hence, we have:

$$(\beta^1)^*(L) - L \; \epsilon \; P \qquad\qquad\qquad (5.16)$$

This is the condition for one sort of Lie symmetry.

6.    THE CARTAN FORM AND THE CONDITION FOR LIE SYMMETRY
      OF A VARIATIONAL PROBLEM

Return to the general setting. Let X,Z be manifolds, L a Lagrangian. For simplicity, we deal with
first order Lagrangians. L is then an n-differential
form (n = dim X) on

$$M^1(X,Z) \quad ,$$

whose covector value is base-like (with respect to the
projection $M^1(X,Z) \rightarrow X$) at each point.

The Cartan form construction replaces L with
another n-form

$$\theta(L)$$

which has important properties. (For the case of n = 1,
it was described by Cartan in the book "Lecons sur les
invariants intégraux". The n-dimensional generalization

was developed by T. Lepage in the 1930's.  See my books
(DGCV, LAQM, VBL, GPS, and Vol. IX) for further work and
extensive applications.)  We shall see that the conditions
for "Lie symmetry" can be described in what I believe is
their simplest form in terms of  $\theta(L)$.

The correspondence

$$L \to \theta(L)$$

is "natural" or "functorial" in an obvious sense.  In
addition, here is a very important property, which forms
what I think of as a modern version of  E. Noether's
theorem on the connection between conservation leaves and
symmetries.

Theorem 6.1.  Suppose that every map

$$\phi: X \to Z$$

is an extremal for the calculus of variations problem
determined by  L.  Then,

$$d\theta(L) \quad = \quad 0 \tag{6.1}$$

For the proof, see GPS, Chapter 4, Theorem 3.1.

Now, we work with the explicit formulas for  $\theta(L)$.
Choose indices as follows:

$$1 \le i,j \le n \quad = \quad \dim \quad X$$

$$1 \le a,b \le m \quad = \quad \dim \quad Z \quad .$$

Let

$$x = (x^i)$$

$$z = (z^a)$$

be coordinates for X and Z. Let

$$(x^i, z^a, z_i^a)$$

be the corresponding <u>Lie coordinate system</u> for $M^1(X,Z)$.
Set:

$$\theta^a = dz^a - z_i^a \, dx^i \qquad\qquad (6.2)$$

The one-forms $\theta^a$ generate a Pfaffian system on $M^1(X,Z)$
called the <u>contact system</u>. Also, set:

$$dx = dx^1 \wedge \ldots \wedge dx^n \qquad\qquad (6.3)$$

$$\theta_i = \frac{\partial}{\partial x^i} \lrcorner \, dx \qquad\qquad (6.4)$$

The Lagrangian L is of the form

$$L(x,z,\partial z)dx \quad , \qquad\qquad (6.5)$$

where

$$L(x,z,\partial z)$$

is the notation for a real-valued function on $M^1(X,Z)$.
Set:

$$L_a^i = \frac{\partial L}{\partial z_i^a} \qquad\qquad (6.6)$$

Here is the formula for the Cartan form $\theta(L)$:

$$\theta(L) = Ldx + L_a^i \theta^a \wedge \theta_i \qquad (6.7)$$

Let

$$\beta: X \times Z \to X \times Z$$

be a diffeomorphism. Let

$$\beta^1: M^1(X,Z) \to M^1(X,Z)$$

be its prolongation. $\beta^1$ preserves the contact system P. Hence, there are relations of the following form:

$$(\beta^1)*(\theta^a) = f_b^a \theta^b \qquad (6.8)$$

$$(\beta^1)*(dx^i) = f_j^i dx^j + f_a^i \theta^a \qquad (6.9)$$

(The coefficients f in (6.8) and (6.9) are real-valued functions on $M^1(X,Z)$.)

Set:

$$f = \det (f_j^i) . \qquad (6.10)$$

Then, we have:

$$\int_X (\partial^1 \phi)*(\beta^1)*(L \ dx) = \int_X (\partial^1 \phi)*(f(\beta^1)*(L) \ dx) \qquad (6.11)$$

Now, the condition that $\beta$ be a Lie symmetry is that the left hand side of (6.11) be equal to

$$\int_X (\partial \phi)*(L \ dx) \qquad (6.12)$$

for each $\phi \in M(X,Z)$. Equating the right hand side of (6.11) and (6.12) gives the following relation:

$$\int_X (\partial^1 \phi)*((L-f(\beta^1)*(L)) \ dx) \ = \ 0 \qquad (6.13)$$

for each $\phi \in M(X,Z)$ .

Theorem 6.1 now implies that:

$$d\theta(L) \ = \ d\theta(f(\beta^1)*(L)) \qquad (6.14)$$

Condition (6.14) is a system of differential equations for $\beta$. This is the set of defining equations for the infinite Lie group of all symmetries of the variational problem defined by the Lagrangian Ldx.

Here is another way of looking at this result. Let G be a group of diffeomorphisms of $X \times Z$. If each $g \in G$ is a symmetry of the variational problem defined by the Lagrangian L, we may say (following Lie) that L defines an integral invariant of G. What we have shown is that an integral invariant defines--via the Cartan form--a differential invariant.

Example.    Arc-length as an integral invariant of the
            group of motions of $R^2$

Continue with the example considered in Section 5. Here,

$$X = Z = R \quad .$$

'or the convenience of comparison with classical notation,
ʼe change  Z  to  Y,  so that  $M^1(X,Z)$  has coordinates

$$(x,y,y') \quad .$$

̇hen,

$$L = \sqrt{1 + y'^2} \; dx \quad .$$

̇he Cartan form is:

$$\omega = \sqrt{1 + y'^2} \; dx + \frac{y'}{\sqrt{1 + y'^2}} \; (dy - y'dx)$$

$$= \frac{dx + y' \; dy}{\sqrt{1 + y'^2}}$$

et  $\beta: X \times Y \to X \times Y$  be a rotation.  The transformation
ʼormulas under  $\beta$  have been worked out in Section 5.
̇sing them, we have:

$$*(\omega) = \frac{\cos \theta \; dx + \sin \theta \; dy + \dfrac{(\cos \theta y' - \sin \theta)}{(\sin \theta y' + \cos \theta)} (\cos \theta dy - \sin \theta dx)}{\sqrt{(1 + y'^2)}/(\cos \theta + \sin \theta \; y')}$$

$$= (\sin \theta \; y' + \cos \theta)(\cos \theta \; dx + \sin \theta \; dy)$$

$$+ (\cos \theta \; y' - \sin \theta)(\cos \theta \; dy - \sin \theta \; dx)/\sqrt{1 + y'^2}$$

$$= \frac{dx + y'dy}{\sqrt{1 + y'^2}}$$

$$= \omega$$

Hence:

The Cartan form itself is invariant.

(The general condition for "integral invariant" requires only that its exterior derivative be invariant.)

This way of interpreting Lie's work on integral invariants leads straight into modern physics and control theory.  I hope to elaborate further in a later publication.

Chapter D

DIFFERENTIAL INVARIANTS AND GROUPS OF
SYMMETRIES OF DIFFERENTIAL EQUATIONS

1.    INTRODUCTION

The book "Differentialgleichungen", by Lie and
Scheffers offers many concrete examples of how (Lie)
group theory may be used to solve ordinary differential
equations.  This material has always fascinated me (since
it is the most direct and concrete area where groups meet
differential equations), and its extension to more compli-
cated and mathematically sophisticated situations is
clearly of great potential interest and applicability.
Note a recent applied mathematics book by Bluman and Cole
[1] concerned with this interaction between Lie theory
and differential equations.  However, judging by the book,
the authors' acquaintence with Lie theory (in either its
classical or modern version) is not very extensive, and
the book can, at best, serve as a collection of interesting examples.

In this chapter I will present a general version of
the material in the Lie-Scheffers book, using the theory
of mapping element spaces described in Chapter A.  We
begin with the simplest example which can serve to
illustrate general principles.

2.    AFFINE SYMMETRIES OF LINEAR, INHOMOGENEOUS SECOND
      ORDER DIFFERENTIAL EQUATIONS

Let $z$ and $x$ denote real variables, $z$ the
dependent, $x$ the independent variable. Consider the
following differential equation:

$$\frac{d^2z}{dx^2} + a(x) \frac{dz}{dx} + b(x)z = c(x) \qquad (2.1)$$

Let $X$ denote the space whose variable is $x$, $Z$
the space whose variable is $z$. (Thus, $X$ and $Z$ are
the real numbers, or an interval of real numbers.)  Let

       $M(X,Z)$

denote the space of maps $X \to Z$, i.e., functions

       $x \to z(x)$ .

We denote a typical element of $M(X,Z)$ by $\underline{z}$.

Consider a one-parameter group of maps $M(X,Z) \to M(X,Z)$
of the following form:

$$\underline{z} \to \underline{z} + t\underline{z}_0 \equiv g(t)(\underline{z}) , \qquad (2.2)$$

where "t" is the group parameter and $\underline{z}_0$ is a fixed
element of $M(X,Z)$. The necessary and sufficient condition
that, for each $t$, $g(t)$ maps solutions of (2.1) into
solutions, is that:

$$\frac{d^2 z_0}{dx^2} + a \, \frac{dz_0}{dx} + b\underline{z}_0 \;\; = \;\; 0 \quad , \tag{2.3}$$

i.e., that $\underline{z}_0$ be what is called classically a __particular__
__solution of the homogeneous equation__ (2.3).

We now show how this one-parameter group of symmetries
of (2.1) leads to a reduction in the order of the differential equation. (In terms of modern computer science
jargon, one would say that the group __leads to a reduction__
__in complexity of the system.__)

Introduce another one-dimensional space Y with
variable y and let

$$M(X,Y)$$

be the space of maps

$$x \rightarrow \underline{y}(x) \quad .$$

Let

$$\phi: \; M(X,Z) \; \rightarrow \; M(X,Y)$$

be the map defined by the following formula:

$$\underline{y} \;\; = \;\; \phi(\underline{z}) \;\; = \;\; \frac{d}{dx} \, (\underline{z}_0^{-1} \, \underline{z}) \tag{2.4}$$

__Theorem 2.1.__ If $\underline{z}$ satisfies the second order, inhomogeneous equation (2.1), and $\underline{z}_0$ is a particular solution
of the second order homogeneous equation (2.3), then

$$\phi(\underline{z})$$

satisfies a first order inhomogeneous differential equation which is determined by (2.1) and $\underline{z}_0$ alone.

Proof. Set

$$\underline{w} = \underline{z}_0^{-1}\underline{z} \quad . \tag{2.5}$$

Then,

$$\frac{d\underline{z}}{dx} = \frac{d}{dx}(\underline{z}_0\underline{w}) = \frac{d\underline{z}_0}{dx}\underline{w} + \underline{z}_0\frac{d\underline{w}}{dx} \tag{2.6}$$

$$\frac{d^2\underline{z}}{dx^2} = \frac{d^2\underline{z}_0}{dx^2}\underline{w} + 2\frac{d\underline{z}_0}{dx}\frac{d\underline{w}}{dx} + \underline{z}_0\frac{d^2\underline{w}}{dx^2} \tag{2.7}$$

Now, $\underline{z}$ satisfies the inhomogeneous equation (2.1), while $\underline{z}_0$ satisfies the homogeneous equation (2.3). Hence,

$$c = \frac{d^2\underline{z}}{dx^2} + a\frac{d\underline{z}}{dx} + b\underline{z}$$

$$= \quad , \text{ using } (2.5)\text{-}(2.7),$$

$$\left(2\frac{d\underline{z}_0}{dx} + a\underline{z}_0\right)\frac{d\underline{w}}{dx} + \underline{z}_0\frac{d^2\underline{w}}{dx^2} \tag{2.8}$$

Now, using (2.4) and (2.5),

$$\underline{y} = \frac{d\underline{w}}{dx} \quad .$$

Hence, we have:

$$\underline{z}_0 \, \frac{d\underline{y}}{dx} + \left( 2 \, \frac{d\underline{z}_0}{dx} + a\underline{z}_0 \right) \underline{y} \;\; = \;\; c \qquad\qquad (2.9)$$

This is the first order, inhomogeneous differential equation which

$$\underline{y} \;\; = \;\; \phi(\underline{z})$$

satisfies.

Theorem 3.2.  Considered as a map

$$\phi: M(X,Z) \rightarrow M(X,Y) \quad ,$$

defined by formula (2.4), and with $\; t \rightarrow g(t) \;$ the one-parameter affine group acting on $\; M(X,Z), \;$ defined by (2.2), we have:

$$\phi(g(t)\underline{z}) \;\; = \;\; \phi(\underline{z}) \qquad\qquad (2.10)$$

$$\text{for all} \;\; \underline{z} \; \epsilon \; M(X,Z) \quad .$$

Proof.  Formula (2.10) is a trivial consequence of (2.2) and (2.4).

$$\phi(g(t)\underline{z}) \;\; = \;\; \frac{d}{dx} \, \underline{z}_0^{-1} (\underline{z} + t\underline{z}_0)$$

$$= \;\; \frac{d}{dx} \, (\underline{z}_0^{-1}\underline{z}) + \frac{d}{dx} \, (t)$$

$$= \;\; \phi(\underline{z}) \quad .$$

Here is the interpretation of all this which is of
the greatest consequence for the theory of differential
equations.

Theorem 3.3. Let $z_0$ be a particular solution of the
homogeneous equation (2.3), so that $t \to g(t)$ defined by
(2.2) is a one-parameter group of symmetries of the
inhomogeneous differential equation (2.1). Let

$$\underline{S} \subset M(X,Z)$$

denote the space of all solutions of the inhomogeneous
second order differential equation (2.1). Let

$$\underline{S}' \subset M(X,Y)$$

denote the space of all solutions $\underline{y}$ of the inhomogeneous
first order differential equation (2.9). Then,

$$\phi(\underline{S}) \;=\; \underline{S}' \tag{2.11}$$

Further, $\phi$ identifies the orbit space of the one-
parameter group

$$t \to g(t)$$

acting on $\underline{S}$ with $\underline{S}'$.

Proof. We have seen already (in the derivation of
Equation (2.9)) that $\phi$ maps $\underline{S}$ into $\underline{S}'$. We must show
that it is onto.

If $\underline{y}$ is a solution of (2.9), let $\underline{w}$ be any
solution of

$$\frac{d\underline{w}}{dx} = \underline{y}$$

Set:

$$\underline{z} = \underline{z}_0\underline{w} \quad .$$

The steps given above, leading from (2.1) to (2.9), are
clearly reversible, to show that $\underline{z}$ must satisfy (2.1),
i.e.,

$$\underline{z} \; \epsilon \; \underline{S} \quad .$$

Since

$$\phi(\underline{z}) = \underline{y} \quad ,$$

we have proved (2.11).

Let us now prove that the fibers of $\phi$ are
precisely the orbits of the one-parameter group $t \rightarrow g(t)$.
Suppose that

$$\underline{z}, \underline{z}_1$$

are two solutions of (2.1), such that:

$$\phi(\underline{z}) = \phi(\underline{z}_1) \quad .$$

Now, $\phi$, as a map

$$M(X,Z) \rightarrow M(X,Y)$$

is linear, hence

$$\underline{\phi}(\underline{z}-\underline{z}_1) = 0$$

Hence,

$$\underline{z}_0^{-1}(\underline{z}-\underline{z}_1) = \lambda \ \varepsilon \ R \quad ,$$

or

$$\underline{z} = \underline{z}_1 + \lambda\underline{z}_0 = g(\lambda)(\underline{z}_1)$$

This shows explicitly that $\underline{z},\underline{z}_1$ lie on the same orbit of the group $t \to g(t)$. ($\lambda$ is the value of $t$ needed to move $\underline{z}_1$ to $\underline{z}$.)

Remark. $\phi$ can be interpreted in terms of a mapping also denoted by $\phi$, from

$$M^2(X,Z) \to M^1(X,Y) \quad .$$

Let $(x,z,z',z'')$ be the Lie coordinates for $M^2(X,Z)$ and let

$$(x,y,y')$$

be the Lie coordinates for $M^1(X,Y)$. $\phi$ also can be considered as a mapping

$$\phi: M^2(X,Z) \to M^1(X,Y) \quad .$$

In fact, here is the formula which does this:

$$\phi(x,z,z',z'') = \left( x,y = \frac{d}{dx} (z_0^{-1})z + z_0^{-1}z', \right.$$

$$\left. y' = \frac{d^2}{dx^2} (z_0^{-1})z + 2 \frac{d}{dx} (z_0^{-1})z' + z_0^{-1}z'' \right)$$

(2.12)

The differential equation (2.1) defines a subset of $M^2(X,Z)$, while the differential equation (2.9) defines a subset of $M^1(X,Y)$. We see that $\phi$, as defined by (2.12), maps one subset into the other. The fibers of this map are the orbits of the one-parameter group that $t \rightarrow g(t)$ defines--via prolongation--on $M^2(X,Z)$.

It is this form of the theory that Lie and Scheffers develop in "Differentialgleichungen". In the next section we go to the general version.

Some general remarks by Vessiot [1] can be readily interpreted in this case. The differential equation on $M^1(X,Y)$ is called the resolvent system. For each solution $\underline{y}$ of this system, the inverse image

$$\phi^{-1}(\underline{y})$$

consists of maps which form are the solution of automorphic differential equations system, with the characteristic property that the solutions are acted on transitively by the given group $t \rightarrow g(t)$.

3.   THE GENERAL LIE THEORY FOR GROUPS OF SYMMETRIES OF ORDINARY DIFFERENTIAL EQUATIONS

Let $X$ and $Z$ be one dimensional manifolds, with variables $x$ and $z$. (In fact, everything readily generalizes to the case where $Z$ is a finite dimensional vector space.) Consider an r-th order differential equation

$$DE \subset M^r(X,Z)$$

as a submanifold of the r-th order mapping element space.

Denote a typical element of $M(X,Z)$ by

$$\underline{z} \quad .$$

Let

$$\partial^r \underline{z}: X \to M^r(X,Z)$$

denote its r-th order prolongation. Let $\underline{S}$ denote the set of solutions of the differential equations, i.e., elements

$$\underline{z} \in M(X,Z)$$

such that

$$\partial^r \underline{z}(X) \subset DE \quad . \tag{3.1}$$

Let $G$ be a group of diffeomorphisms of

$$X \times Z \quad .$$

Let $G^r$ denote the prolonged group of diffeomorphisms, acting on

$$M^r(X,Z) \quad .$$

Definition. $G$ is a group of symmetries of the differential equation if each element of $G^r$ maps the subset $DE \subset M^r(X,Z)$ into itself.

Suppose that  G  satisfies this condition.  Let  Y
be another one-dimensional manifold, with variable  y,
and let  s  be an integer less than  r.

Definition.  A map

$$\phi: M^r(X,Z) \to M^s(X,Y)$$

is said to be a decomposition map relative to the action
of  G  and the differential equation, if the following
conditions are satisfied:

> $\phi$  is onto

> The fibers of  $\phi$  are the orbits of  $G^r$.

> If  $\underline{z} \in M(X,Z)$,  then there is an element
> $\underline{y} \in M(X,Y)$  such that

$$\phi(\partial^r \underline{z}) = \partial^s \underline{y} \quad . \tag{3.2}$$

Such a map  $\phi$  now defines an s-order differential
equation

$$(DE)' \subset M^r(X,Y) \quad .$$

Just define

$$(DE)' = \phi(DE) \tag{3.3}$$

(Of course, assume that  (DE)'  is a submanifold.  Lie
always implicitly makes such optimistic assumptions.)

Let $\underline{S}'$ be the set of solutions of this differential equation, i.e., the space of maps

$$\underline{y} \in M(X,Y)$$

such that

$$\partial^S \underline{y}(X) \subset (DE)' \qquad\qquad (3.4)$$

We can now define a map

$$\delta: M(X,Z) \to M(X,Y) \qquad\qquad (3.5)$$

by the following formula:

$$\delta(\underline{z}) = \pi\phi(\partial^r \underline{z}) \quad , \qquad\qquad (3.6)$$

where $\pi$ is the projection map $M^S(X,Y) \to Y$. Alternately, the following property holds:

$$\partial^S \delta(\underline{z}) = \phi(\partial^r(\underline{z}) \qquad\qquad (3.7)$$

$\delta$ is a <u>non-linear differential operator</u>.

<u>Theorem 3.1.</u>

$$\delta(\underline{S}) \subset \underline{S}' \quad . \qquad\qquad (3.8)$$

<u>Proof.</u>  In fact, this is a triviality.  Given $\underline{z} \in \underline{S}$, use (3.7):

$$\partial^S \delta(\underline{z})(X) = \phi(\partial^r \underline{z})(X)$$

$$\phi(\partial^r \underline{z})(X))$$

To say that $\underline{z} \in \underline{S}$, i.e., that $\underline{z}$ is a solution of DE, is to say that

$$\partial^r \underline{z}(X) \subset DE \quad .$$

Using (3.3), we have that:

$$\phi(\partial^r \underline{z}(X)) \subset (DE)' \quad ,$$

which implies that $\delta(\underline{z})$ is a solution of (DE)'.

We see now that we have reproduced, in an abstract, general form, the situation that we found in a special case in Section 2. We now turn to put another, special, classical situation in the same framework.

4.    INTEGRATING FACTORS FOR FIRST ORDER, ORDINARY
      DIFFERENTIAL EQUATIONS

Specialize the situation to the case

$$r = 1 \quad .$$

Let the differential equation be of the following form:

$$\frac{dz}{dx} = h(x,z) \tag{4.1}$$

Let $\theta$ be the following one-form on $X \times Z$:

$$\theta = dz - h \, dx \tag{4.2}$$

Thus, the graph of a solution of (4.1), considered as a curve in $X \times Z$ is a solution curve for the Pfaffian system

$$\theta = 0 \quad .$$

Conversely, any such solution curve on which $dx$ is linearly independent defines a solution of (4.1).

Definition. An integrating factor for the differential equation (4.1) is a function $f$ on $X \times Z$ such that:

$$d(f\theta) = 0 \tag{4.3}$$

If such an $f$ can be found, then one can follow the classical procedure and, using only what Lie calls "permissable operations" (i.e., "quadratures") find a function $k$ on $X \times Z$ such that:

$$dk = f\theta \tag{4.4}$$

Such a $k$ then defines a conserved function for the differential equation (4.1) (classical terminology: Integral function). Explicitly, an element $z \in M(X,Z)$ satisfies the differential equation (4.1) if and only if:

$$\frac{d}{dx} \left( k(x, \underline{z}(x)) \right) = 0 \tag{4.5}$$

Example. Linear inhomogeneous equations

Suppose that the differential equation (4.1) takes the following special form:

$$\frac{dz}{dx} = a(x)z + b(x) \tag{4.6}$$

Then,

$$\theta = dz - (az+b)dx \quad .$$

Let $\underline{z}_0$ be a particular solution of the homogeneous equation:

$$\frac{d\underline{z}_0}{dx} = a\underline{z}_0 \tag{4.7}$$

Then, it is readily seen that:

$$d(\underline{z}_0^{-1}\theta) = 0 \quad .$$

Set:

$$k(x,z) = \underline{z}_0^{-1}z + \int b(x) \ dx \tag{4.8}$$

It is readily seen that:

$$dk = \underline{z}_0^{-1}\theta \tag{4.9}$$

Thus, $\underline{z}_0^{-1}$ is the integrating factor for $\theta$, while $k$ is the conserved function. For a solution $x \rightarrow \underline{z}(x)$ of (4.6), we have:

$$\frac{d}{dx} k(x,\underline{z}(x)) = 0 \quad ,$$

i.e.,

$$\frac{d}{dx} (z_0^{-1}\underline{z}) + b = 0 \tag{4.10}$$

We recognize that, in this case, the "integrating factor" method of solution is identical to the group-theoretic method presented in Section 2.

Return to the case of a general equation (4.1).
Let $k(x,z)$ be a conserved function constructed with the
aid of an integrating factor $f$.

Introduce another space $Y$. Define the map

$$\phi: M^1(X,Z) \to M(X,Y)$$

by the following formula:

$$\phi(x,z,z') = (x, y \equiv z') \ . \tag{4.11}$$

Introduce the following relation on $M(X,Y)$:

$$\frac{\partial k}{\partial x} + \frac{\partial k}{\partial z} (x,z)y = 0 \tag{4.12}$$

We see that a $\underline{z} \in M(X,Z)$ is a solution of the differential equation (4.1) if and only if:

$$\delta \underline{z} \equiv \phi \partial^1(z)$$

<u>satisfies the relation</u> (4.12).

In this situation we have followed the same pattern
as in Section 2--giving the "integrating factor" determines
a differential operator--in this case $\delta$--which converts
the first order differential equation into a "zero-th order"
one. Again, using such information to lower the order is
typical of Lie's approach.

Let us now turn to study another situation. As
Cartan did in "Lecons sur les invariants intégraux", we
convert Lie's formulation of the problem into a <u>Pfaffian</u>
<u>system</u> framework.

5. A PFAFFIAN SYSTEM FRAMEWORK IN WHICH TO STUDY FIRST
   ORDER DIFFERENTIAL EQUATIONS

Let us abstract from the situation encountered in
Section 4, and postulate the following data:

   a) A 3-dimensional manifold M with coordinates
      $(x,y,z)$.
   b) A one-form $\theta$ on M.
   c) A vector field A on M.
   d) A function f on M.

(To correlate with previous work, think of M as $M^1(X,Z)$.
However, "x,y,z" do not necessarily have the same meaning
as in earlier work.)

We suppose the following conditions are satisfied:

$$A(f) = 0 \qquad (5.1)$$

$$A(\theta) = h\theta ,$$
$$\qquad (5.2)$$
$$\text{for some function } h \in F(m)$$

Our aim is to study the one-dimensional solution
manifolds of the Pfaffian system generated by

$$\theta, f .$$

Denote this set by $\underline{S}$.

(5.1) and (5.2) tell us that the one-parameter group
G of diffeomorphisms generated by A map a solution
manifold into another solution manifold. We want to

examine the orbit space

$$G \setminus \underline{S} \quad ,$$

and, if possible, show that it can be exhibited as the
space of all solutions of another Pfaffian system.

Let us choose the coordinate system $(x,y,z)$ for
M so that

$$A = \frac{\partial}{\partial z} \tag{5.3}$$

(It is well-known that this can always be done <u>locally</u>
if, as we implicitly assume, A is non-zero at each point.
Lie would think of this as do-able using "permissable
operations", because, once the explicit formulas for G
are known, finding this special coordinate system only
involves using the implicit function theorem.)

After at most changing $\theta$ by a non-zero scalar
factor (which will not affect $\underline{S}$), we can suppose that:

$$A(\theta) = 0 \quad . \tag{5.4}$$

Suppose then that, in terms of this coordinate system
which is specially adapted to A, $\theta$ takes the following
form:

$$\theta = adx + bdy + cdz \quad , \tag{5.5}$$

where $(a,b,c)$ are functions on M.

Relations (5.1), (5.3) and (5.4) now imply that:

$$f,a,b,c \text{ are functions of } (x,y) \text{ alone} \tag{5.6}$$

We can now readily analyze $\underline{S}$:

Case 1.   c = 0

In this case, the Pfaffian system determining $\underline{S}$ is of the following form:

$$
\begin{aligned}
a(x,y)dx + b(x,y)dy &= 0 \\
f(x,y) &= 0
\end{aligned}
\tag{5.7}
$$

$\underline{S}$ then consists of the functions $x \to \underline{y}(x), \underline{z}(x)$ which satisfy the following conditions:

$$
\begin{aligned}
\frac{d\underline{y}}{dx} &= -\frac{a}{b} \\
f(x,\underline{y}) &= 0 \\
\underline{z}(x) &\text{ is arbitrary}
\end{aligned}
\tag{5.8}
$$

The action of  G  on  $\underline{S}$  is then as follows:

$$
(\underline{y},\underline{z}) \to (\underline{y},\underline{z}+t)
\tag{5.9}
$$

Remark. This is a sort of "singular" situation.

<u>Case 2</u>.  $c \neq 0$

We can then divide by  c,  to normalize  $\theta$  so that:

$$\theta = dz + adx + bdy .$$ (5.10)

<u>S</u>  then consists of the functions

$$x \rightarrow \underline{y}(x), \underline{z}(x)$$

satisfying the following conditions:

$$
\begin{array}{l}
\dfrac{d\underline{z}}{dx} = -a(x,\underline{y}(x)) - b(x,\underline{y}(x)) \dfrac{d\underline{y}}{dx} \\[3mm]
f(x,\underline{y}(x)) = 0
\end{array}
$$ (5.11)

<u>Remark</u>.  Notice that (5.11) is in a form that is solvable "by quadratures".  $x \rightarrow \underline{y}(x)$  is determined by using the implicit function theorem applied to the second equation in (5.10) (if  $\partial f/\partial y \neq 0$,  which would be the "non-singular" situation), and then  $\underline{z}$  is obtained by an integration once the expression for  $\underline{y}$  is substituted into the first equation in (5.11).  This is a typical feature of Lie's work:  Given a first order differential equation and a vector field which leaves it invariant, in the coordinate system in which the vector field takes it "canonical form", the differential equation is solvable "by quadratures".

We can now readily examine the action of  G,   the
one-parameter group generated by  A,   on  $\underline{S}$.  Since  A
is in its canonical form (5.3), the action of  G  is as
follows:

$$
\boxed{
\begin{array}{l}
\underline{y} \rightarrow \underline{y} \\[2ex]
\underline{z} \rightarrow \underline{z} + t
\end{array}
}
\tag{5.12}
$$

To calculate the orbit space

$$G \setminus \underline{S} \quad ,$$

map:

$$M(X, Y \times Z) \rightarrow M(X,Y)$$

via the Cartesian projection, i.e., for

$$(\underline{y}, \underline{z}) \; \varepsilon \; M(X, Y \times Z) \quad ,$$

$$(\underline{y}, \underline{z}) \rightarrow (\underline{y}) \quad .
\tag{5.13}$$

Call this map  $\phi$.  Then,  $\phi$,  applied to a solution
$(\underline{y}, \underline{z})$  of (5.10) sends it into a solution of the following
zero-th order differential equation

$$f(x, \underline{y}(x)) \; = \; 0
\tag{5.14}$$

Note that:

The fibers of $\phi$, considered as a
map :$\underline{S} \to$ (solutions of (5.14)), are
the orbits of $G$.

Hence:

The orbits of $G$ on $\underline{S}$ are the
solutions of a zero-th order differential equation.

Again, these remarks amount to another formulation
of Lie's idea that a symmetry group of a differential
equation can be used to lower the order. (In computer
science terms, this probably means to lower the degree
of complexity.)

We now turn to the study--with similar methods--of
second order ordinary differential equations.


6.    SECOND ORDER ORDINARY DIFFERENTIAL EQUATIONS WHICH
      ADMIT ONE-PARAMETER GROUPS OF SYMMETRIES

Consider a four-dimensional space, with variables
labelled as:

$$(x,z,z',z'') \quad .$$

Suppose given a function

$$f(x,z,z',z'')$$

of these variables.  It determines a second-order differ-

ential equation.  A solution is an element

$$z \in M(X,Z)$$

such that:

$$f\left(x, \ \underline{z}, \ \frac{d\underline{z}}{dx}, \ \frac{d^2\underline{z}}{dx^2}\right) = 0 \qquad (6.1)$$

Introduce the following one-form:

$$\theta_1 = dz - z'dx \qquad (6.2)$$

$$\theta_2 = dz' - z''dx \qquad (6.3)$$

Let  A  be a vector field of the form:

$$A = a(x,z) \frac{\partial}{\partial x} + b(x,z) \frac{\partial}{\partial z} \qquad (6.4)$$

The prolongations of A,  denoted by:

$$A' = A + c(x,z,z') \frac{\partial}{\partial z'} \qquad (6.5)$$

$$A'' = A' + d(x,z,z',z'') \frac{\partial}{\partial z''} \ , \qquad (6.6)$$

should be familiar.  They satisfy the following Lie

derivative relations:

$$A'(\theta_1) = \text{(a multiple of } \theta_1)$$

$$A''(\theta_2) = \text{(a linear combination of } \theta_1, \theta_2) \ .$$

<u>Definition</u>.  A  generates a <u>one-parameter group of symme-</u>
<u>tries of the differential equation</u> (6.1) if the following
condition is satisfied:

$$A''(f) = 0 \qquad\qquad\qquad (6.7)$$

Let  G  be the one-parameter group generated by  A
and let  <u>S</u>  denote the set of solutions of (6.1).  As in
previous work in this chapter, our problem is to compute
the orbit space

$$G \setminus \underline{S} \quad ,$$

and to show that it is determined by solving lower order
differential equations and "quadratures".  To this end, let

$$(u,v)$$

be new coordinates for  X × Z,  chosen so that the vector
field  A  takes its canonical form:

$$A = \frac{\partial}{\partial z} \quad .$$

We can then choose Lie coordinates

$$(u,v,v',v'')$$

for  $M^2(X,Z)$,  i.e.,

$$v' = \frac{dv}{du} ; \qquad v'' = \frac{d^2v}{du^2} \quad .$$

The prolongation  A''  of  A  is, in these new coordinates,
just:

$$A'' = \frac{\partial}{\partial v} \tag{6.8}$$

f  becomes a function

$$F(u,v,v',v'')$$

of these new variables.  The differential equation (6.1)
is converted to the following equation in these new
variables:

$$F\left(u, \underline{v}, \frac{d\underline{v}}{du}, \frac{d^2\underline{v}}{du^2}\right) = 0 \quad . \tag{6.9}$$

Now relation (6.7)--expressing the fact that  A
generates a one-parameter group of symmetries of the
differential equation--is obviously independent of coordinates.  Hence,

$$A''(F) = 0 \quad .$$

But, given (6.8), this means that:

F  is independent of  v.

Thus, the differential equation (6.1), in these new
coordinates, takes the following form:

$$F\left(\underline{u}, \frac{d\underline{v}}{du}, \frac{d^2\underline{v}}{du^2}\right) = 0 \tag{6.10}$$

Set:

$$\underline{y} = \frac{d\underline{v}}{du} \quad . \tag{6.11}$$

Then, the second order differential equation (6.1) has
been mapped, via the correspondence

$$\underline{z} \rightarrow \underline{v} \rightarrow \underline{y} \quad \equiv \quad \frac{d\underline{v}}{du}$$

into its <u>first order</u> differential equation:

$$F\left(u, \ \underline{y}, \ \frac{d\underline{y}}{du}\right) \ = \ 0 \qquad\qquad (6.12)$$

Again, we see appearing the typical feature of Lie's work--
a one-parameter group of symmetries of the differential
equation has been used to <u>lower the complexity</u> of the
differential equation.

We can recapitulate in the following geometric way.
Let  $\underline{S}$  denote the set of solutions of the second order
differential equation (6.1).  We begin with

$$\underline{S} \subset M(X,Z) \quad .$$

With the aid of the coordinates  $(u,v)$,  map

$$X \times Z \ \rightarrow \ U \times V \quad .$$

$S$  becomes a subset

$$\underset{\sim}{S'} \subset M(U,V) \quad .$$

$\partial^2$  maps  $\underline{S'} \rightarrow M(U,M^2(U,V))$.  Map

$$M^2(U,V) \ \rightarrow \ M^1(U,Y)$$

as follows:

$$(u,v,v',v'') \rightarrow (u, \ y=v', \ y'=v'') \quad . \qquad (6.13)$$

Let

$$\underline{S}'' \subset M(U,Y)$$

be the space of solutions of the <u>first order</u> equation (6.12).
Then, we see that the map (6.13) sends

$$\underline{S}' \rightarrow \underline{S}'' \quad .$$

<u>The fibers of this mapping are precisely the orbits of the</u>
<u>one-parameter group generated by the diffeomorphism</u> A.
Again, this decomposition of the space of solutions of a
differential equation is typical of Lie's work (and
Vessiot's extension of it.)

<u>Remark</u>. Here is another way Lie thinks of this. Consider
the coordinates $(u,v)$ such that A takes it canonical
form $\partial/\partial v$. Then,

$$A'' = \frac{\partial}{\partial v} \quad .$$

Hence, the functions

$$(u,v',v'')$$

are <u>second order differential invariants</u> of the one-
parameter group generated by A. They form a <u>basis</u> for
such invariants, in the sense that any other invariant is
a function of them. In particular, any <u>invariant second</u>
<u>order differential equation</u> is a function of them. This

leads to the reduction to a first order differential
equation.

This is obviously only the beginning of what should
be a very general theory, with the differential equation
(6.1) replaced by more general ones and the single vector
field  A  replaced by Lie algebras of vector fields.  We
now treat another example, also considered in "Differentialgleichungen" by Lie and Scheffers.


7.    SECOND ORDER ORDINARY DIFFERENTIAL EQUATIONS WHICH
      ADMIT TWO-DIMENSIONAL LIE ALGEBRAS OF SYMMETRIES

Let  $(x,z)$  be coordinates of  $X \times Z$.  Let
$(x,z,z',z'')$  be Lie coordinates of  $M^2(X,Z)$.  Suppose
given the following data:

a)   A second order differential equation

$$f(x,z,z',z'') \ = \ 0 \eqno(7.1)$$

b)   Two vector fields  $A_1, A_2$  on  $X \times Z$,
     whose prolongations  $A_1'', A_2''$  leave invariant
     the relation (7.1), and which form a two-
     dimensional Lie algebra.

Again, the method to be followed is to choose new
coordinates  $(u,v)$  for  $X \times Z$  so that the vector fields

$A_1$, $A_2$ take their canonical form. Now, the canonical
form for finite dimensional Lie algebras of vector fields
acting on two-dimensional manifolds has been developed by
Lie. (See "Transformationsgruppen", Vol. III, by Lie
and Engel, or the previous volume in this translation
series.) In this case, the situation is particularly
simple:

Case 1.

$$[A_1, A_2] = 0 \qquad\qquad\qquad (7.2)$$

One can then choose coordinates $(u,v)$ such that:

$$A_1 = \frac{\partial}{\partial u} , \qquad A_2 = \frac{\partial}{\partial v} . \qquad\qquad (7.3)$$

Suppose that, in these coordinates, the differential
equation (7.1) takes the following form:

$$F(u,v,v',v'') = 0 \qquad\qquad\qquad (7.4)$$

The prolongations of $A_1$, $A_2$ can be readily calculated
from (7.2):

$$A_1'' = \frac{\partial}{\partial u} , \qquad A_2'' = \frac{\partial}{\partial v} \qquad\qquad (7.5)$$

The functions

$$(v', v'')$$

are then a basis for the <u>second order differential invariants</u>

of the group $G$ generated by $A_1$, $A_2$. If the relation
(7.4) is to be invariant under this group, it is definable
by a relation of the form:

$$F(v', v'') = 0 \qquad (7.6)$$

The differential equation (7.1) is then, in terms of
these coordinates, of the form:

$$F\left(\frac{dv}{du}, \frac{d^2 v}{du^2}\right) = 0 \qquad (7.7)$$

Set:

$$y = \frac{dv}{du} \qquad (7.8)$$

Then, (7.6) becomes:

$$F\left(y, \frac{dy}{du}\right) = 0 \qquad (7.9)$$

This is a first order differential equation which is
solvable by the method of separation of variables, i.e.,
by "quadratures".

      We can sum up as follows:

Theorem 7.1. Let $G$ be the two-dimensional (abelian) Lie
group of diffeomorphisms of $X \times Z$ generated by $A_1, A_2$.
Let $S$ be the space of solutions of the second order,
ordinary differential equation (7.1). Then, the orbit space

$$G \setminus \underline{S}$$

is identified with the space of all solutions of the differential equation (7.9).

Case 2.

$$[A_1, A_2] = A_2, \qquad A_2 = h A_1 , \qquad (7.10)$$

for some function  h.

Choose coordinates  (u,v)  so that

$$A_1 = \frac{\partial}{\partial v} .$$

Then,

$$\frac{\partial h}{\partial v} = h ,$$

or

$$\log h = v + \text{function of}\ u ,$$

or

$$h = k(u) e^v \frac{\partial}{\partial v}$$

$$A_2 = k(u) e^v \frac{\partial}{\partial v} . \qquad (7.11)$$

The coordinate system  (u,v)  can then be chosen so that either

$$A_1 = \frac{\partial}{\partial v} , \qquad A_2 = v \frac{\partial}{\partial v} \qquad (7.12)$$

or

$$A_1 = \frac{\partial}{\partial v} \; , \qquad A_2 = uv \frac{\partial}{\partial v} \qquad (7.13)$$

<u>Remark</u>. This assumes that $dk/du \equiv 0$, or $\neq 0$ at the point in question. It is, of course, typical of Lie's work that the "singular" intermediate cases are put to the side. In fact, it would be very interesting and important to go over Lie's work, being more careful about these possibilities.

If either (7.11) or (7.12) are satisfied,

$$A_1'' = \frac{\partial}{\partial v} \; . \qquad (7.14)$$

In case (7.11) is satisfied,

$$A_2'' = v \frac{\partial}{\partial v} + v' \frac{\partial}{\partial v'} + v'' \frac{\partial}{\partial v''} \qquad (7.15)$$

In case (7.13) and (7.14) are satisfied, we see that the differential equation (7.1) can be written in the following form:

$$F(u,(v''/v')) = 0 \qquad (7.16)$$

This is of the type which is solvable "by quadratures". In this case:

The orbit space $G \setminus \underline{S}$ is the space
of all solutions $\underline{v} \in M(U,V)$ of

$$F\left(u, \frac{d^2v}{du^2} \middle/ \frac{dv}{du}\right) = 0$$

If (7.13) is the canonical form, then the conclusion is only slightly modified. The details are left to the reader.

If $\underset{\sim}{G}$, the Lie algebra of vector fields on $X \times Z$ spanned by $A_1, A_2$, does not satisfy Case 1 or Case 2, then it is readily seen that (with certain "singular" cases put to the rule) it acts transitively, and coordinates $(u,v)$ can be chosen so that $\underset{\sim}{G}$ is equivalent to the two-dimensional solvable Lie group acting on itself by left translation. The orbit space

$$G \setminus \underline{S}$$

is then readily computed, by similar methods. Details are left to the reader.

8.   GENERAL REMARKS ABOUT GROUPS OF SYMMETRIES OF SECOND ORDER ORDINARY DIFFERENTIAL EQUATIONS

Let $X, Z$ be one-dimensional manifolds, and let

$$DE \subset M^2(X,Z) \tag{8.1}$$

be a codimension-one submanifold, i.e., a second order ordinary differential equation.

Let $\underset{\sim}{G}$ be a Lie algebra of vector fields on $X \times Z$.
Let

$$\underset{\sim}{G}''$$

be the Lie algebra of vector fields on $M^2(X,Z)$ which
results from prolonging the action of $\underset{\sim}{G}$. $\underset{\sim}{G}$ is said to
__act as symmetries on the differential equation__ (8.1) if,
at each point of DE, $\underset{\sim}{G}''$ is tangent to the submanifold DE.
If this condition is satisfied, then Lie proves ("Differentialgleichungen", Theorem 39, p. 405) that:

$$\dim \underset{\sim}{G} \; \leq \; 8 \quad .$$

If $\dim \underset{\sim}{G} = 8$, then Lie also shows that

$$G \; = \; \text{projective group,} \quad SL(3,R),$$
$$\text{acting on} \quad X \times Z \equiv PS(R^3).$$

For each Lie subgroup of $SL(3,R)$, one can then
find __all__ second order differential equations invariant
under the subgroup. I __believe__ that Lie has shown that
the general case is locally equivalent to one of this type.
Then, Lie's methods lead very beautifully to a general
(local) structure theory of second order ordinary differential equations and their groups of symmetries.

9.    LIE'S PROBLEM FROM CARTAN'S EXTERIOR DIFFERENTIAL
      SYSTEM VIEWPOINT

One can abstract from these calculations the following general framework. Let  M  be a manifold, and let

        I

be a differential ideal of differential forms on  M.  Let
n  be an integer  (n < dim M), and let

        S

be the space of n-dimensional manifolds of  M  such that
each form of  I  is identically zero when restricted to
the submanifold.  Such a submanifold is called a solution
submanifold of  I.  (The usual terminology,  e.g., in
Cartan, is integral submanifold.  I believe it is better
to try to eliminate the term "integral", which has a very
archaic meaning.)

Let  G  be a group of diffeomorphisms of  M,  such
that:

        g*(I)  =  I
        for all  g ε G.

If  G  satisfies this condition, it is called a group of
symmetries of the system  I.  It obviously acts on  S,
i.e., the transform of  s ε S  by a  g ε G  is again a
solution submanifold.

The goal of the Lie Cartan theory is to
"parameterize" the orbit space

$$G \setminus \underline{S} \quad .$$

The usual way of doing this is to construct another manifold IM', with a system I', and solution manifolds $\underline{S}'$,
and a map

$$\phi : \underline{S} \to \underline{S}' \quad ,$$

such that the fibers of $\phi$ are "generically" the orbits
of G. I' is called the resolvent system.

In general, G will be an "infinite Lie group".
(See Lie's papers on this subject in a later volume of
this series of translations.) How to implement all this
is a challenge to us!

Chapter E

## THE GALOIS-PICARD-VESSIOT THEORY OF LINEAR
## ORDINARY DIFFERENTIAL EQUATIONS

1.    INTRODUCTION

As we have seen, much of Lie's work was <u>motivated</u>
by his goal of extending the Galois theory of algebraic
equations to differential equations. Partly inspired by
Lie's ideas, Picard and Vessiot created an analogue of
Galois theory for linear ordinary differential equations.
(The best classical expositions are in Picard's "Cour
d'analyse", [1] or the "Encyclopédie" article of Vessiot
[1].)  In recent times, this material has been enormously
elaborated and developed abstractly in the context of
"Differential algebra". (See Kolchin [1].) From the
point of view of understanding its implications for the
theory of <u>differential equations</u>, this has not been the
most fruitful development!

In this chapter I will return to the older work,
and develop the ideas in the context of differential
equation theory, emphasizing the connection with Lie's
concept of <u>differential invariant</u>. A 1900 article by
G. Fano [1] has been very useful in this task.  (I am
indebted to R. Risch for this reference, and further
instruction in the Picard-Vessiot theory.)

2.    THE LIE-VESSIOT FORM OF A LINEAR ORDINARY SCALAR
      DIFFERENTIAL EQUATION

All vector spaces in this chapter will have the
complex numbers as field of scalars. t will denote a
real parameter, varying over a certain interval of real
numbers which will be denoted by T.

Let Z be a finite dimensional vector space. $M(T,Z)$
denotes the space of maps

$$\underline{z}: t \to \underline{z}(t) \quad \text{of} \quad T \to Z \quad .$$

Definition. An n-th order, linear, scalar ordinary
differential operator

$$D: M(T,Z) \to M(T,Z)$$

is a C-linear operator of the following form:

$$D(\underline{z}) = \frac{d^n \underline{z}}{dt^n} + a_{n-1}(t) \frac{d^{n-1} \underline{z}}{dt^{n-1}} + \cdots + a_0 \underline{z} \qquad (2.1)$$

In (2.1), the coefficients $a_1, \ldots, a_{n-1}$ are fixed
maps $T \to C$. Until further notice, we suppose a differential operator of the form (2.1) is given and fixed. $\underline{S}$
denotes the space of its solutions.

Theorem 2.1. Suppose $\underline{z} \in \underline{S}$ is such that the vectors

$$\underline{z}(t), \frac{d\underline{z}}{dt}(t), \ldots, \frac{d^{n-1} \underline{z}}{dt^n}(t)$$

are linearly independent for one value $t_0$ of t. Then, these vectors are linearly independent (hence form a basis for Z) for _each_ value of t.

The _proof_ is left as an exercise for the reader. In classical terms, the proof involves the _Wronskian_ of the functions which are the components of z in a fixed basis for Z. (Recall that the Wronskian satisfied a linear homogeneous first order equation, so that if it vanishes at one point it vanishes everywhere.) Actually, the proof can be done without use of the Wronskian, and as such is a nice illustration of the elegant use of "intrinsic" vector space methods instead of the cumbersome classical linear equation methods using determinants.

Theorem 2.2. S is a vector space of dimension $n^2$.

The _proof_ is again left as an exercise.

Use this result to impose a manifold structure on S, (any finite dimensional vector space has a natural manifold structure.)

Theorem 2.3. Let $S^0$ denote the elements $z \in S$ which lie in no proper linear subspace of Z. Then, $S^0$ is an open non-empty subset of S. (Its complement in S is an algebraic subset of S.)

Proof. To say that $\underline{z} \in \underline{S}$ lies in a proper linear subspace of $Z$ is to say that there are at most $(n-1)$ linearly independent vectors among the

$$\{\underline{z}(t): t \in T\}$$

This implies that

$$\underline{z}(t), \frac{d\underline{z}}{dt}(t), \ldots, \frac{d^{n-1}\underline{z}}{dt^n}(t)$$

are linearly dependent for each $t$.

Using Theorem 2.1 and 2.2, we conclude that $\underline{z} \in \underline{S}$ lies in a proper linear subspace of $Z$ if and only if the vectors

$$\underline{z}(t_0), \frac{d\underline{z}}{dt}(t_0), \ldots, \frac{d^{n-1}\underline{z}}{dt^n}(t_0)$$

are linearly dependent for one value $t_0$ of $t$. This sub-set clearly forms a subset of $\underline{S}$ which is defined by the vanishing of certain algebraic equations, hence is a closed subset of $\underline{S}$. Its complement--which is $\underline{S}^0$--is then an open subset of $\underline{S}$.

Let $M^r(T,Z)$ denote the r-th order mapping elements associated to maps $T \to Z$. A Lie coordinate system for $M^n(T,Z)$ can be denoted by

$$t, z, z', \ldots, z^{(n)} .$$

If $\underline{z} \in M(T,Z)$, and if

$$\partial^n \underline{z} : \ T \to M^n(T,Z)$$

is its prolongation, then

$$z \ = \ \underline{z}(t), \ z' \ = \ \frac{d\underline{z}}{dt} \ , \ldots, \ z^{(n)} \ = \ \frac{d^n\underline{z}}{dt}$$

are its coordinates.

For fixed $t$, $M^n(T,Z)$ is a vector space of dimension $(n+1)n$, with the maps

$$z,\ldots,z^{(n)} : \ M^n(T,Z) \to Z$$

linear maps.

Recall the concept of <u>rational map between finite dimensional vector spaces</u>. (See Volume VIII of IM, for example.)

<u>Definition</u>. A map

$$\alpha : \ M^n(T,Z) \to C$$

is said to be <u>rational</u> and <u>time-independent</u> if there is a <u>rational map</u> (in the algebro-geometric sense)

$$\beta : \ \underbrace{Z \times \cdots \times Z}_{\text{(n+1) copies}} \to C$$

such that

$$\alpha(t,z,z',\ldots,z^{(n)}) \ = \ \beta(z,z',\ldots,z^{(n)}) \qquad (2.2)$$

$$\text{for all} \ \ (t,z,z',\ldots,z^{(n)}) \in M^n(T,Z)$$

<u>Theorem 2.4</u>.  There are time-independent, rational maps

$$\alpha_0, \ldots, \alpha_{n-1} : M^n(T,Z) \to C$$

such that:

$$
\begin{aligned}
\alpha_0(\partial^n \underline{z}(t)) &= a_0(t) \\
&\vdots \\
\alpha_{n-1}(\partial^n \underline{z}(t)) &= a_{n-1}(t)
\end{aligned}
\tag{2.3}
$$

for <u>all</u>  $\underline{z} \in \underline{S}^0$,  all  $t \in T$.

<u>Proof</u>.  Given  $\underline{z} \in \underline{S}$,  it satisfies the differential equation:

$$a_0 \underline{z} + a_1 \frac{d\underline{z}}{dt} + \cdots + a_{n-1} \frac{d^{n-1}\underline{z}}{dt^n} = - \frac{d^n \underline{z}}{dt^n} \tag{2.4}$$

Choose a fixed basis for  $Z$,  and identify  $\underline{z}$  with its components  $(z_1(t), \ldots, z_n(t))$  with respect to this basis. When this is substituted into (2.4), it may be considered as a set of  $n$  linear equations, with  $n$  <u>unknowns</u>  $a_0, \ldots, a_{n-1}$.  The coefficients are determined linearly by the  $z_1(t), \ldots, z_n(t)$  and their <u>derivatives</u>.  The condition that  $\underline{z} \in \underline{S}^0$  is that the  $n \times n$  matrix coefficients of these equations be non-singular, i.e., have non-zero determinant. (This determinant is the classical <u>Wronskian</u>.) Written in this  $n \times n$  scalar form, it can be solved by the usual Cramer's Rule formulas, to express $a_0, \ldots, a_{n-1}$ in terms of the components of

$$z = (z_1, \ldots, z_n)$$

$$z' = (z_1', \ldots, z_n')$$

$$z^{(n-1)} = (z_1^{(n-1)}, \ldots, z_n^{(n-1)}) \quad .$$

The expressions which occur in these formulas are rational functions of these coordinates, which we <u>define</u> as $\alpha_0, \ldots, \alpha_{n-1}$. It is important for later purposes to note specifically their time-independence.

<u>Remark</u>. What we have done is essentially to re-express the original differential equation

$$D(\underline{z}) = 0$$

in a non-linear, rational, but partially <u>time-independent</u> form, expressed by the $\alpha_0, \ldots, \alpha_{n-1}$. In fact, we see that the argument given above is reversible, and a $\underline{z} \in M(T, Z)$ which lies in no proper linear subspace of $Z$ is a solution of $D(\underline{z}) = 0$ if and only if:

$$\alpha_0(\partial^n \underline{z}) = a_0$$

$$\vdots \tag{2.5}$$

$$\alpha_{n-1}(\partial^{n-1}\underline{z}) = a_{n-1}$$

Notice that the explicit time dependence has been segregated
on the right hand side of (2.5), of course, at the expense
of making the equations highly non-linear in form.  Vessiot,
in his great Encyclopédie article [1], mentions this as a
typical Lie idea.  In this form, (2.5) is recognized as an
automorphic system, in the sense of Lie and Vessiot, i.e.,
two solutions $\underline{z}, \underline{z}'$ of (2.5) differ by the action of a
group on  $Z$,  namely the group  $GL(Z)$  of invertible
linear maps  $Z \to Z$.  We call it the Lie-Vessiot form of the
equations.

Examples. We can make these rational maps  $\alpha$  explicit in
the lowest dimensional cases.

Case 1.  $n = 1$

          The differential equation becomes:

$$a_0 \underline{z} = -z'  .$$

Hence,

$$\alpha_0(z, z') \equiv -\frac{z'}{z} = a_0$$

Case 2.  $n = 2$

          Identify  $\underline{z}$  with components  $(z_1, z_2)$.  The equations
are:

$$a_0 z + z_1 z' = -z''  ,$$

or

$$a_0 z_1 + a_1 z_1' = -z_1''$$

$$a_0 z_2 + a_1 z_2' = -z_2''$$

Using Cramer's Rule for solving linear equations:

$$a_0 = \frac{\begin{vmatrix} -z_1'' & z_1' \\ -z_2'' & z_2' \end{vmatrix}}{\begin{vmatrix} z_1 & z_1' \\ z_2 & z_2' \end{vmatrix}} \equiv \alpha_0(z,z',z'')$$

$$a_1 = \frac{\begin{vmatrix} z_1 & -z_1'' \\ z_2 & -z_2'' \end{vmatrix}}{\begin{vmatrix} z_1 & z_1' \\ z_2 & z_2'' \end{vmatrix}} \equiv \alpha_1(z,z',z'')$$

3.    THE GALOIS GROUP ACCORDING TO THE IDEAS OF LIE AND
      VESSIOT

Let us recapitulate the notation and results of
Section 2.  Z  is an n-dimensional complex vector space.
T  is an interval of real numbers.  $M^n(T,Z)$  is the space

of n-th order mapping elements  : $T \rightarrow Z$.

$$\alpha_0, \ldots, \alpha_{n-1}: M^n(T,Z) \rightarrow C$$

are rational, time-independent maps.

These maps have the following group-invariance property.

Let  $GL(Z)$  denote the group of vector
space automorphisms

$$g: Z \rightarrow Z  .$$

Extend  $GL(Z)$  to act on  $T \times Z$  as follows:

$$g(t,z)  =  (t,  g(z))  .$$

Prolong this action to an action on  $M^n(T,Z)$,
in accordance with the usual Lie rules.  Then
$GL(Z)$,  so prolonged, leaves the maps
$\alpha_0, \ldots, \alpha_n$  invariant, i.e.,

$$\alpha_0 g  =  \alpha_0$$
$$\vdots \qquad\qquad\qquad\qquad (3.1)$$
$$\alpha_{n-1} g  =  \alpha_0$$

for  $g \ \varepsilon \ GL(Z)$

The differential equation

$$D\underline{z}  =  0$$

has been rewritten in its Lie-Vessiot form, namely:

$$\alpha_0 (\partial^n \underline{z}) \;=\; a_0$$

$$\vdots \tag{3.2}$$

$$\alpha_n (\partial^n \underline{z}) \;=\; a_1 \quad ,$$

where $a_0, \ldots, a_{n-1}$ are the scalar functions of $t$, which occur in the linear differential operator $D$.

(3.1) and (3.2) make it <u>evident</u> that the differential equation

$$D = 0$$

is <u>invariant</u> under the action of $GL(Z)$; namely, if

$$\underline{z} \;\varepsilon\; \underline{S} \;, \quad g \;\varepsilon\; GL(X) \quad ,$$

then

$$g(\underline{z}): t \rightarrow g(\underline{z}(t))$$

belongs to $\underline{S}$. (Of course, this was clear in the original $D\underline{z} = 0$ form also. We will see, however, that (3.2) is in a better form for applying Galois ideas.)

So far, we have taken for granted the existence-uniqueness theorems for ordinary differential equations of type

$$D\underline{z} = 0 \;.$$

Suppose we concern ourselves with <u>how</u> the solutions are to be obtained, in terms of the properties of the coefficients $a_0, \ldots, a_{n-1}$. It is very difficult to understand what is meant

by this on the basis of pure logic.  Roughly, one wants to
know when solutions can be generated from the coefficients
$a_0, \ldots, a_{n-1}$ in terms of certain types of algorithms.  The
specific algorithms to be used seem to be conditioned by
the long history of trying to "solve" differential equations.
In particular, solution "by quadratures" is the classical
technique.  The great accomplishment of Picard and Vessiot
was to invent a suitable and tractable way of "algebraciz-
ing" this concept.  Nowadays, this involves what is called
a <u>differential field</u>.

Suppose (for simplicity) that the  $a_0, \ldots, a_{n-1}$  are
meromorphic functions of the variable  t.  Let

$$\Omega$$

denote the set of functions of  t  obtained from the
$a_0, \ldots, a_{n-1}$  by applying rational functions in the a's and
<u>their derivatives</u>.  $\Omega$  forms a <u>differential field</u>, i.e.,
$\Omega$  forms a field, in the usual sense of algebra, and in
addition, is closed under derivation  $a \to da/dt$.  ($\Omega$  is
the <u>smallest differential field</u> containing the a's.)

Fix an element

$$\underline{z} \ \epsilon \ \underline{S}^0$$

Let RR denote the set of rational, time-independent maps

$$\alpha: M^n(T, Z) \to C$$

which have the following property:

For each $\underline{z} \varepsilon \underline{S}^0$, the function

$$t \rightarrow \alpha(t, \partial^n \underline{z}(t)) \tag{3.3}$$

belongs to $\Omega$.

As we have seen,

$$\alpha_0, \ldots, \alpha_{n-1} \varepsilon \text{ RR} . \tag{3.4}$$

An element $\alpha \varepsilon \text{RR}$ is called a rationality relation for the solutions of $D = 0$.

Now we come to the main point.

Definition.  The Galois group of the equation $D = 0$ (with respect to the "rationality domain" $\Omega$) is the subgroup of $g \varepsilon \text{ GL}(Z)$ such that:

$$\alpha g = \alpha \tag{3.5}$$

for all $\alpha \varepsilon \text{ RR}$

Here is a statement (I will not go into the proof) of the Main Theorem of Galois Theory :  If a time-independent rational map

$$\alpha: M^n(T, Z) \rightarrow C$$

satisfies the following condition:

$$\alpha g = \alpha \tag{3.6}$$

for all $g \varepsilon$ (Galois group)   ,

then  $\alpha \varepsilon$ RR. In other words, the time-independent, rational n-th order <u>differential invariants</u> (in the sense of Lie) are the rationality relations for the differential equation  D = 0.

## 4.    SOLVABILITY OF THE GALOIS GROUP AND SOLVABILITY OF THE DIFFERENTIAL EQUATION "BY QUADRATURES"

We can now <u>use</u> the Main Theorem to explain the famous relation quoted in the title of this section.

Now, the Galois group  G--as a closed subgroup of GL(Z)--is a Lie group. We <u>suppose</u>, for simplicity, that it is <u>connected</u> and <u>solvable</u>.

<u>Remark</u>.  E Kolchin [1] lifted the restriction that it be connected. It is easy to see that  G  is an <u>algebraic subgroup</u> of  GL(Z),  i.e., it is defined by algebraic equations. He then proved that such <u>solvable algebraic groups</u> could be put into triangular matrix form. (Lie's original proof only applied to connected Lie groups.) This gave a major impetus to the theory of algebraic groups, which soon developed methods independent of the classical Lie methods.

By Lie's theorem on Solvable Lie Algebras, there is a basis for  Z  so that the matrices of  G  with respect to this basis take a <u>triangular form</u>. Let

$$z_1, \ldots, z_n$$

be a basis for $Z^d$ with respect to which $G$ takes its tri-
angular form.  Then,

$$g(z_1, \ldots, z_n) \;=\; (\bar{z}_1, \ldots, \bar{z}_n) \quad,$$

with:

$$
\begin{aligned}
\bar{z}_1 &= a_1^1 z_1 \\[1mm]
\bar{z}_2 &= a_2^1 z_1 + a_2^2 z_2 \\[1mm]
&\;\;\vdots
\end{aligned}
\tag{3.7}
$$

The coefficients $a$ in (3.7) are the matrix of $g$ with
respect to this basis.  In particular, they are <u>constants</u>.
Thus we have:

$$\frac{d}{dt} \log z_1$$

is invariant under $G$; (i.e., $z_1^1/z_1$ is invariant).  By the
Main Theorem, if $\underline{z} = (\underline{z}_1(t), \ldots, \underline{z}_n(t))$ is a solution in $\underline{S}$,
then there is a $b(t) \; \varepsilon \; \Omega$ such that:

$$\frac{d}{dt} \log \underline{z}_1 \;=\; b(t) \quad,$$

i.e.,

$$\underline{z}_1(t) \;=\; e^{\int b(t)\, dt} \tag{3.8}$$

The first component of the solution is then given "by quadratures", in formula (3.8).

Let us similarly show that $z_2$ is given by iterated quadratures. Set:

$$W(z_1, z_2) = \begin{vmatrix} z_1 & z_2 \\ z_1' & z_2' \end{vmatrix}$$

Then,

$$W(\bar{z}_1, \bar{z}_2) = cW(z_1, z_2) \quad ,$$

where $c$ is a constant. Hence,

$$\frac{d}{dt} \log W(z_1, z_2)$$

is invariant under the Galois group $G$.

By the Main Theorem, there is a function $b_1(t) \; \varepsilon \; \Omega$ such that:

$$\frac{d}{dt} \log W(\underline{z}_1, \underline{z}_2) = b_1(t) \quad ,$$

or

$$W(\underline{z}_1, \underline{z}_2) = e^{\int b_1(t)\, dt} \tag{3.9}$$

But, the left hand side of (3.9) is:

$$\frac{d\underline{z}_1}{dt} z_2 - \frac{d\underline{z}_2}{dt} z_1 \quad .$$

Equating this to the right hand side of (3.9) determines (keeping in mind that $\underline{z}_1(t)$ is determined by (3.8)) $z_2$ as the solution of a first order, inhomogeneous differential

equations, which is again solvable "by quadratures".  Continuing in this way, we see that we generate an iterative algorithm
for generating the solution  $\underline{z} = (\underline{z}_1(t),\ldots,\underline{z}_n(t))$   of   $D = 0$
by quadratures.

Our main aim in this chapter--showing how the Galois
group in the Picard-Vessiot theory is related to Lie's
Differential Invariants--has been accomplished.


4.       A GALOIS THEORY FOR A LINEAR FIRST ORDER PARTIAL
         DIFFERENTIAL OPERATOR

The only systems for which there seems to be a "Galois
theory" in a reasonably precise sense are the algebraic equations and the linear, scalar-coefficient ordinary differential
equations, i.e., the Picard-Vessiot case.  For these systems,
the "symmetry group" of the system is a Lie group, i.e., is
finite dimensional.  From the point of view of applications,
it would be most interesting to apply the Galois ideas to
partial differential equations.  Presumably, this stands to
the Picard-Vessiot case as the theory of infinite Lie groups
stands to the theory of finite parameter Lie groups.  There
is extensive literature in the period 1890-1910 by Lie,
Vessiot and Drach developing such a theory, but it is all
rather vague and wordy.  Perhaps only now are we in possession
of sufficiently powerful and accurate differential geometric

tools and notation to do the job correctly!  (However, it will
still be extremely difficult to make solid mathematics of it.)
As a beginning, I will develop the special case described by
the title of this section, which was a favorite example for
discussion by Lie, Vessiot and Drach.   (Note also the paper
by E. Cartan, "La theorie de Galois et ses généralisations",
Comm. Math. Helv., 11 (1938), 9-25 ≡ Oeuvres, Pt. III,
Vol. I, p. 123.  Cartan states that he wrote it in this
early period;  it contains very brief and cryptic discussion
of a number of very interesting examples.)

Let  X  be a manifold, with coordinates

$$(x^i) , \quad 1 \leq i,j \leq n = \dim X .$$

Let

$$A = a^i \frac{\partial}{\partial x^i}$$

be a non-singular vector field on  X,  which we will consider
as fixed.

Associate with  A  the first order, linear partial
differential equation

$$a^i \frac{\partial f}{\partial x^i} = 0 . \tag{4.1}$$

Our goal is to develop a "Galois theory" for this equation.
As in the case of a scalar ordinary differential equation,
the first step is to convert it into an equivalent system,

which Vessiot calls <u>automorphic</u> in the sense that a group acts transitively on the solutions.  (In the Picard-Vessiot case, this amounts to replacing

$$\frac{d^n y}{dt^n} + \cdots + a_n y = 0 \quad ;$$

to be solved for a scalar function $t \to y(t)$, by a system

$$\frac{d^n \underline{z}}{dt^n} + \cdots + a_n \underline{z} = 0 \quad ,$$

to be solved for an n-dimensional vector valued $t \to \underline{z}(t) \in Z$ function of $t$.  The group $GL(Z)$ then acts <u>transitively</u> on the space of solutions.)

     This can be done in the following way:

     Replace (4.1) by the system

$$A(y^i) = \delta_1^i \tag{4.2}$$

$$\equiv \begin{cases} 0 & \text{if } i \neq 1 \\ 1 & \text{if } i = 1 \end{cases}$$

Write

$$\underline{y} = (y^1, \ldots, y^n) \quad .$$

$\underline{y}$ is then a map $X \to R^n$.

     This is the map that sends the vector field $A$ into its "canonical form:

$$\frac{\partial}{\partial y^1} \quad . \qquad\qquad\qquad (4.3)$$

Let G be the group of diffeomorphisms of $R^n$ which
preserves the vector field (4.3). Then two solutions of
(4.2) can be transformed into each other by an element of
G, i.e., (4.2) is the appropriate "automorphic system",
and G is the appropriate "group of symmetries" of this
automorphic system. (It replaces GL(Z) in the Picard-
Vessiot case.)

Recall the next step in the Picard-Vessiot case;
replacing the equation

$$D\underline{z} \;=\; 0$$

with an equivalent non-linear system, with the coefficients
of D on the right hand side. We can do that in this case
also.

For, suppose $(y^i) = \underline{y}$ is a solution of (4.2) which
is "generic" in the sense that

$$\det \left( \frac{\partial y^i}{\partial x^j} \right) \;\neq\; 0 \quad .$$

We can then apply the inverse function theorem, and write the
equation in the following form:

$$\frac{\partial x^i}{\partial y^1} \;=\; a^i \qquad\qquad\qquad (4.4)$$

Remark.  We are using tensor analysis conventions.  $\partial x^i/\partial y^1$ (usually) denotes the function obtained by inverting the relation

$$v \to \underline{y} \quad ,$$

and expressing  x  as a function of  y,  differentiating with respect to  $y^i$, then going back to X-space and writing it as a function of  x!  These equations are equivalent to (4.2), of course

We can interpret this in the following more abstract way.  Let

$$DIFF \ (X,Y)$$

be the space of diffeomorphisms

$$\underline{y}: X \to R^n \quad .$$

Let

$$\alpha^i: DIFF \ (X,Y) \to F(X)$$

be the first order (highly non-linear!) differential operator such that:

$$\alpha^i(\underline{y}) \quad = \quad \frac{\partial x^i}{\partial y^1} \tag{4.5}$$

The differential equation (4.2) can then be written in the following Lie-Vessiot form:

$$\alpha^i(\underline{y}) \quad = \quad a^i \tag{4.6}$$

Remark. $\alpha^i$ can also be interpreted as a map on a portion
of the mapping element space $M^1(X,Y)$; namely, that portion
on which the linear map on tangent vectors to $X$ to tangent
vectors to $Y$ is one-one. This is analogous to the role
played by "time-independent, rational maps" in the Picard-
Vessiot case. It is also related to "Eulerian jets" which
appear in my discussion of fluid mechanics in GPS.

Now, we can indicate how to set up a Galois theory.
Let $G$ be the group of diffeomorphisms $Y \to Y$ <u>which leaves</u>
<u>invariant the vector field</u> $\partial/\partial y^1$. Let $G$ act on DIFF $(X,Y)$
in the obvious way:

> If $g \in G$, $\underline{y} \in$ DIFF $(X,Y)$, then the
> translate of $\underline{y}$ by $g$ is the composite
> map $g\underline{y}$.

Now, note the following crucial property of the differential
operators $\alpha^i$:

> $\alpha^i(g\underline{y}) = \alpha^i(\underline{y})$
>
> for $y \in$ DIFF $(X,Y)$, $g \in G$.

This makes precise the sense in which $G$ <u>acts as a group</u>
<u>of symmetries on the differential equation</u> (4.2).

We must now pick out a subgroup of $G$ (determined
by the coefficients $a^1, \ldots, a^n$) which is to be called the
<u>Galois group of the equation</u> (4.2). I am not sure that I

really know how this is to be done.  Presumably, one could
write down some sort of "axioms" for the functorial assignment

   $A \to$ (subgroup of group of diffeomorphisms of $R^n$)  ,

which might have a unique solution.

Instead, I will proceed in a more cautious way,
based on the procedure used for the Picard-Vessiot theory.

Let $\Omega$ be some set of functions on $X$, closed under
partial derivatives and algebraic operations, and <u>containing</u>
$a^1, \ldots, a^n$. This is the <u>domain of rationality</u>.

<u>Fix</u> a $\underline{y}_0 \in \text{DIFF }(X,Y)$, which satisfies (4.6), i.e.,
a "generic" solution of equations (4.2).  Let RR be the set
of (non-linear) differential operators

$$\alpha: \text{DIFF }(X,Y) \to F(X)$$

such that:

$$\alpha(\underline{y}_0) \in \Omega$$

Let $G_0$ be the subgroup of all $g \in G$ such that:

$$\alpha(g\underline{y}) = \alpha(\underline{y})$$

for all $\underline{y} \in \text{DIFF }(X,Y)$, all $\alpha \in \text{RR}$

$G_0$ is called the <u>Galois group</u> of the equation (4.1)!

Now, this is rather a wild mathematical object!  One
could, perhaps, hope that a <u>finite number</u> of such $\alpha$'s could
be used to define $G_0$.  (Lie and his students believed in

such "finiteness" conditions, and Tresse [1] seems to have
given the most complete proof available.  I cannot follow it.
Presumably, it is a question of proving a generalization of
the "Hilbert basis theory" to cover differential invariants.
There is also much work in this century on "differential
algebra", by Ritt and his students, which seems to be oriented
in this direction.  I cannot follow this either.)  Then,  $G_0$
would be a Lie subgroup of the infinite Lie group  G,  i.e.,
a subgroup defined by a system of partial differential equations.  (See Kumpera and Spencer [1] for a definitive account
of what is known about these objects in present day mathematics.)  E. Cartan has developed methods for studying such
subgroups in the papers on Infinite Lie Groups in Vol. 2,
Part II of his Oeuvres, but this material is also hidden in
the mists of mathematical obscurity!

I hope I have written enough to convince the reader
that progress in developing a "Galois Theory" for partial
differential equations is closely linked to the theory of
Infinite Dimensional Lie Groups.  There will be more about
this in later volumes of Translations and Comments on Lie's
work.

BIBLIOGRAPHY

[1] R. Abraham and J. Marsden, Foundations of Mechanics, W.A. Benjamin, N.Y., 1967.

[1] W. Blascke, Vorlesungen über Integralgeometrie, B.G. Teubner, 1936.

[1] G. Bluman and J. Cole, Similarity methods for differential equations, Springer-Verlag, N.Y., 1974.

[1] E. Cartan, Oeuvres Complètes, Gauthier-Villars, Paris, 1955.

[2] E. Cartan, Les éspaces à connexion projective, Gauthier-Villars, Paris, 1937.

[3] E. Cartan, Lecons sur les invariants intégraux, Hermann, Paris, 1923.

[1] C. Chevalley, Theory of Lie groups, Princeton University Press, 1946.

[1] G. Darboux, Théorie générale des surfaces, Chelsea Publishing Co., Bronx, N.Y., 1972.

[1] G. Fano, Math. Ann. (1900), p. 568.

[1] G. Fano and E. Cartan, La théorie des groupes continus et la géométrie, Encyclopédie des Sciences Math., reprinted in Cartan's Ourvres, Part 3, Vol. 2.

[1] H. Federer, Geometric measure theory, Springer-Verlag, N.Y., 1969.

[1] R. Hermann, Existence in the large of parallelism homomorphisms, Trans. Amer. Math. Soc., 161 (1963), pp. 170-.83.

[2] R. Hermann, Cartan connections and the equivalence problem for geometric structures, "Contributions to differential equations", 3 (1964), pp. 199-248.

[3] R. Hermann, Equivalence of submanifolds of homogeneous spaces, Math. Ann., 158 (1965), pp. 284-289.

[4] R. Hermann, On the foundations of Integral Geometry, Ren. Cir. Math. de Palermo, 9 (1960), pp. 91-96.

271

[5]   R. Hermann, Infinite dimensional Lie algebras and
      current algebras, Proceedings of the 1969 Battelle-
      Seattle Rencontres on Mathematical Physics, Springer-
      Verlag, Berlin, 1970, pp. 312-337.

[6]   R. Hermann, Lie algebras and quantum mechanics, W.A.
      Benjamin, N.Y., 1970 (Abbr.: LAQM).

[7]   R. Hermann, Differential geometry and the calculus of
      variations, Academic Press, N.Y., 1969 (Abbr.: DGCV).

[8]   R. Hermann, Vector bundles in mathematical physics,
      Parts I and II, W.A. Benjamin, N.Y., 1970 (Abbr.: VB).

[9]   R. Hermann, Geometry, physics and systems, Marcel Dekker,
      N.Y., 1973 (Abbr.: GPS).

[10]  R. Hermann, Interdisciplinary Mathematics, Vols. I-X,
      1973-75, Math Sci Press, Brookline, Mass. (Abbr.: IM).

[11]  R. Hermann, Sophus Lie's 1880 Transformation Group
      Paper, Math Sci Press, Brookline, Mass. (Abbr.: LG, Vol. 1)

[1]   I. Kaplansky, An introduction to differential algebra,
      Hermann, Paris, 1957.

[1]   E. Kolchin, Differential algebra and algebraic groups,
      Academic Press, N.Y., 1973.

[1]   A. Kumpera, Invariants differentiels d'un pseudogroupe
      de Lie, Journal of Diff. Geom., 10 (1975), pp. 347-416.

[1]   A. Kumpera and D.C. Spencer, Lie equations, Princeton
      University Press, 1972.

[1]   S. Lie, Differentialgleichungen, Chelsea Publishing Co.,
      Bronx, N.Y., 1967.

[1]   S. Lie and F. Engel, Theorie der transformationsgruppen,
      Vols. 1-3, Chelsea, N.Y., 1970.

[1]   S. Lie and G. Scheffers, Vorlesungen uber continuerliche-
      gruppen, Chelsea, N.Y., 1971.

[1]   E. Picard, Traité d'Analyse, Gauthier-Villars, Paris, 192

[1]   L. Pontrjagin, Topological groups, Gordon and Breach,
      N.Y., 1966.

[1]   A. Sagle and R. Walde, Introduction to Lie groups and
      Lie algebras, Academic Press, N.Y., 1973.

[1]   H. Samelson, Notes on Lie algebras, Van Nostrand-
      Reinhold, N.Y., 1969.

[1]   L. Santalo, Introduction to integral geometry, Hermann,
      Paris, 1953.

[1]   M. Spivak, A comprehensive introduction to differential
      geometry, Vols. 1-5, Publish or Perish, Boston, Mass.

[1]   N. Steenrod, Topology of fiber bundles, Princeton
      University Press, 1950.

[1]   A. Tresse, Acta Math., 18 (1894).

[1]   E. Vessiot, Méthodes d'integration élémentaires,
      Encyclopédie des sciences mathématiques, Tome II, Vol. 3,
      Teubner, Leipzig, 1910.

[1]   E. Wilczynski, Projective differential geometry of curves
      and ruled surfaces, B.G. Teubner, Leizig, 1906.

[1]   G. Witham, Linear and non-linear waves, Wiley, N.Y., 1974.